Good Food
for Everyone Forever

A people's takeover of the world's food supply

BY THE SAME AUTHOR

The Link: Uncovering Our Earliest Ancestor

The Secret Life of Birds: Who They Are and What They Do

Feeding People Is Easy

The Secret Life of Trees: How They Live and Why They Matter

So Shall We Reap: the Concept of Enlightened Agriculture

In Mendel's Footnotes: Genes and Genetics from the 19th century to the 22nd

The Variety of Life: A Survey and a Celebration of All the Creatures That Have Ever Lived

Neanderthals, Bandits, and Farmers

The Day Before Yesterday

The Engineer in the Garden: Genes and Genetics from the Idea of Heredity to the Creation of Life

Last Animals at the Zoo

Global Ecology

Food Crops for the Future

The Food Connection

Future Cook

The Famine Business

COLIN TUDGE

Good Food
for Everyone Forever

A people's takeover of the world's food supply

Written on behalf of

 The Campaign for Real Farming

Pari
Publishing

A catalogue record for this book is available
from the British Library

ISBN 9788895604138
Printed and bound in Italy

Book and cover design by Andrea Barbieri

Cover images:
© Viorika Prikhodko, Jon Helgason, Michael Valdez, Sergej Petrakov,
Valentyn Volkov /iStockphoto

Finito di stampare nel mese di marzo 2011
presso Grafiche Vieri, Roccastrada (GR)
per conto di Pari Publishing S.a.s. di Eleanor F. Peat & C. - Pari (GR)

Pari Publishing

Via Tozzi 7, 58045 Pari (GR), Italy
www.paripublishing.com

TABLE OF CONTENTS

PREFACE

This book can be seen as a revised, updated, and greatly extended version of *Feeding People is Easy*, first published by Pari Publishing in 2007. But events have moved ahead so rapidly over the past three years that I feel the book needs to be re-presented under a new title. At least, the bedrock ideas have not changed (the earlier chapters are very similar to the original) but the world has changed and so has the practical strategy that's now being proposed—which is what really counts.

For it has become more and more clear to me that the kinds of changes in food and farming that the world now desperately needs will not be brought about by what we might call 'the powers-that-be' (an expression nicked from St Paul although he used it in a quite different context). The powers-that-be include modern governments, elected or otherwise; the corporates; and the big banks. They operate in concert, all subscribing to the global economic dogma of neoliberalism on the one hand (the ultimately competitive, allegedly 'free' global market) and finance capitalism on the other (which gives everything a price and then operates the economy as a game of money).

The big three power groups, with their intellectual and expert advisers, all apparently believe that the economic system works, even though it very obviously does not; or else believe that although it does not, it will do if we carry on with more of the same, which is a wondrous but surely most unjustified demonstration of faith. But the structure and the modus operandi of the present system are such that the powers-that-be become ever more powerful, and ever more deeply entrenched. Thus they become less and less able to change their ways, even if they wanted to, which in truth they have no great motivation to do. The conclusion must be that if we, Ordinary Joes, people who give a damn, want the world to be radically different—which it must be if our children and our grandchildren, and other people's children, and our fellow creatures, are to survive in a tolerable form beyond the next few decades—we have to take matters into our own hands.

With this in mind, in 2009, I and various associates formed the Campaign for Real Farming—subtitled, 'A people's takeover of the world's food supply'. This may seem ridiculously grandiose, vainglory writ large. But actually, once we see what the task entails and approach it step by step, it is surely do-able. Already, all around the world, we see initiatives of many different kinds, some huge and some tiny, that are leading us in the necessary directions. The key to success is merely to identify the enterprises and ideas that are truly helpful and to bring about some degree of coordination. There is generally no need to confront the powers-that-be head on. We merely need to start doing things differently. There is no need to try to convert the unconverted. We merely need to find the people and the enterprises that are already on side. There is no need for a majority. We merely need a critical mass of people who give a damn and can see what needs doing—and the necessary numbers already exist. The critical mass is not yet critical only because, as things are, it does not cohere.

The aim of the Campaign is to bring people together, and to develop the necessary ideas further, via a series of conferences which are already in train, and through the campaign website: www.campaignforrealfarming.org. We want the website in turn to metamorphose by degrees into a bona fide college—perhaps to be called 'The College for Enlightened Agriculture' and perhaps more broadly to be called 'The College for the New Agrarianism'. Either way, in the fullness of time the college could and should become a bricks-and-mortar establishment, with its own model farm (and preferably a network of such colleges and farms). In the medium term, the necessary courses can be developed in existing centres of education (some of whom have already expressed interest). In the immediate term, and already up and running, the website can already be seen as a virtual college, where people are coming together, and the necessary ideas are identified and developed.

This book, then, is a gallop through the necessary, basic ideas— as *Feeding People* was. But it also outlines the way forward: at least the first steps on the way to the people's takeover. All this is spelled out in the last third of the book, which is quite new; and since the thesis is potentially life changing (if the vaunting ambition starts to come about), it does seem to justify a new title. So here we have it: *Good Food for Everyone Forever*.

Colin Tudge, Wolvercote, May 31 2010

Why me— and why this book?

In the early 1970s food technologists, alias food processors, strategically poised between a growing band of nutritionists on the one hand and the newly industrial agriculturalists on the other, seemed to bestride the world. They were the scions and the heralds of science, with all its exactitude; and they were driven by the most unimpeachable principle of morality—nothing less than a desire to feed the human race. Above all, they declared in those far off days, people need protein, and the only realistic way to supply it was via 'TVPs'—textured vegetable protein: a form of all-purpose chow spun from the protein of beans (mostly soya, but others too including broad beans) or of algae, fungi, or even bacteria that would be fed on surplus oil (for in those days the world's oil was perceived to be boundless). More broadly the food technologists were wont to say that farmers should think of their crops and livestock not in traditional terms—not as wheat, olives, Hereford cattle or Rhode Island chickens—but as raw materials for processing. This is where the future lay.

I like to get up early, and think. One summer dawn in 1974, gently rocking on our children's garden swing, it occurred to me that if everything the food technologists, nutritionists, and industrial agriculturalists were saying was actually true, then we would all be dead. Instead, at that time, the human population was growing faster than ever, at around two per cent per year—so much so that 'overpopulation' vied with the Cold War in the imminence and perceived magnitude of its threat. Yet most people hadn't yet had a sniff of TVPs, and the 'Green Revolution', based on new varieties of wheat and rice, had yet to make its impact. I had been educated as a biologist and was steeped in scientific orthodoxy—I had left university less than a decade before—but I realized in that moment, one of true epiphany, that all the official lore from on high, from government-approved high-tech industry, was as near as makes no difference the most absolute nonsense. Traditional farming could do with some help no doubt but it had nonetheless enabled the human race to flourish over the previous 10,000 years as no other species ever had; and traditional cooking, which the processors were so keen to replace with their own high-tech concoctions, was beyond improvement. Either the powers-that-be were seriously misguided—just plain wrong—or they were lying.

More than three decades later, genetic engineering has come of age and the powers-that-be—governments, agribusiness, scientists, and technologists, supported by economists, lawyers, and that new brand of bureaucrats known as MBAs—are queuing up to tell us that we will all starve unless we learn to love GMOs (genetically modified organisms, where 'organisms' means crops and livestock). 'GMO' has replaced 'TVP'as the high-tech buzzword for salvation. It was nonsense then and it is nonsense now. Meanwhile the power within the food industry has shifted, particularly in Britain, away from the processors and towards the supermarkets; and whereas the economies of the early 1970s were varied (capitalism took many forms, while China and the USSR both had centralized, planned economies) the whole world now is hooked on or entrapped by the alleged advantages and joys of the global free market. Many have grown very rich from the high-tech, industrialized and increasingly globalised food supply chain; but they have become rich at the expense of humanity as a whole, and other species, and of this Earth, where we all live. The powers-that-be hold out the promise of boundless wealth for all if only we continue as we are, but that perhaps, in a finite world, is the greatest nonsense of all.

The message of this book, I modestly claim, is the most important that can be conceived: that we, human beings, can feed ourselves to the highest standards both of nutrition and of gastronomy; that we can do so effectively forever—for the next 10,000 years, or indeed the next million; that we can do this without cruelty to livestock and without wrecking the rest of the world and driving other species to extinction; and that if we do the job properly, we will thereby create human societies that are truly agreeable, co-operative and at peace, in which all manner of people with all kinds of beliefs and aspirations can be personally fulfilled. The approach is not to replace traditional ways of life and know-how with government-backed, industrialized high tech, buoyed by battalions of salaried experts and intellectuals, but to build upon the traditional crafts: get to know them and understand them; help them along with science of a truly appropriate kind; and practice them in societies that are intended to be agreeable. Craft is what's needed, as was always the case: but craft aided by science. The present perception of modernity—all labour performed by machines, all controlled from above—in truth belongs to the 19th century. The future lies with 'science-assisted craft'—if, that is, we are to have a tolerable future at all.

But to achieve this we, humanity, must bypass and generally sideline the powers-that-be. The world's most powerful governments, industries, and their attendant experts and intellectuals have their minds set on quite different goals, and are pulling in quite different directions—to a large extent completely opposite to what is really required. To be sure, the title of this book is a little hyperbolic: the human population will reach 9 billion by 2050 and it won't exactly be easy to feed everybody to the highest standards. Yet it should be well within our grasp. Indeed this goal is so obviously achievable that it would surely be extraordinarily remiss not to give it a try. In this book I will explain how. But the harder task by far is to bypass the powers-that-be. To do what needs doing we have to re-invent democracy, or rather to make it work almost for the first time in the history of civilization, for the chief rule of democracy—that we should be able to get rid of our 'leaders' when they cease to function on our behalf—has gone missing. 'They' do not know how to run the world, but they do know how to hang on to power. In the last chapter, I will be addressing this, too. Revolution is not required. Renaissance is what's needed—and that is very achievable.

For my own part, I am not a country boy by birth—I was born in London in World War II—but I feel I am a farmer genetically. One side of the Tudge tribe have always been farmers—some were distinguished cattle-breeders—although I belong to the side that got kicked off the land, and became miners. I first became seriously interested in food and farming in the early 1960s, when I was reading zoology at Cambridge (although wasting too much time on cooking). Later I worked for various magazines and for the BBC, who very kindly paid for me to travel and to eat in nice places, and I got to know many of the world's finest cuisines at first hand. I also worked for a time for *Farmers Weekly,* which I treated as an apprenticeship, and for *New Scientist*, and then for several years wrote scientific reports for what was then the Agriculture and Food Research Council, and subsequently for other agricultural institutions including Rothamsted (the oldest dedicated agricultural research institute in the world) and IPGRI (the International Plant Genetic Resources Institute), and spent time at research stations such as ICRISAT (the International Crops Research Institute for the Semi-Arid Tropics), in Hyderabad, India. So I have talked to farmers, agricultural scientists and policy makers in dozens of countries in every continent where farming is practiced (all except Antarctica) and attended or spoken at dozens of conferences. These included the World Food Conference in Rome in 1974—where I was shocked to find that the world's big nations did not set out to solve the problem in hand (of how to feed people) but simply to demonstrate that whatever was going wrong was not their fault, and that they should not be called upon to do more than they were doing already. In the early days, too, when my children were young and we lived in South London, I grew vegetables and kept chickens and got very involved in self-sufficiency. My first book was about farming—*The Famine Business*, published in 1977—and most of my books since have been on related issues, such as *Crop Plants for the Future* in (1988) and *Future Cook* (aka *Future Food*) in 1980, and *Neanderthals, Farmers, and Bandits* in 1998 on the origins of farming. The latest were *So Shall We Reap* in 2003 and *The Secret Life of Trees* in 2005, which discusses the growing and encouraging vogue of agroforestry.

All the time I have been arguing that the root cause of all the world's food problems has nothing to do with shortcomings of humanity, or with the innate inhospitality of planet Earth, and everything to do with policy. Largely, I have felt myself talking to the deaf. But along the way too I have met a great many people who agree with the general thesis of this book, and some of them are seriously well-informed. Professor Bob Orskov, now at the Macaulay Institute, Aberdeen, has been a guru—he has been giving me excellent advice since the early 1970s. In more recent years I have expanded my thinking enormously from conversations with Professor Martin Wolfe, who was previously at the Plant Breeding Institute, Cambridge (before it was privatized) and is now with the Organic Research Centre, and carries out pioneering work with agroforestry in Suffolk. Sir Crispin Tickell has been unfailingly encouraging, and provided many sharp insights. I have also learned a great deal from farmers and thinkers including Roland Bonney and Ruth Layton of the Food Animal Initiative, Oxford; Tim Waygood and Sam Henderson of Agrarian Renaissance, Hertfordshire; Professor Tim Lang; Geoffrey Cannon; Peter Bunyard; Satish Kumar of Schumacher College in Devon; Robin and Binka le Breton of the Iracambi Rainforest Research Center in the Atlantic Rainforest of Brazil; Patrick Krause of the Crofters' Federation, Scotland; Fred Pearce; Derek Cooper and Sheila Dillon of the BBC; and various luminaries at the Soil Association including Peter Melchett, Craig Sams, Helen Browning, and Patrick Holden. Also a few years ago I married Ruth West, who is a lively thinker and critic and has kept me on my intellectual and moral toes. In 2009 Ruth and I established the Campaign for Real Farming; and in January 2010 we teamed up with Graham Harvey to mount the Oxford Real Farming Conference—which we hope will be the first of many.

Recently, certainly in Britain and the United States, I have felt the tide turning. More and more people, including some in high places, are acknowledging that the powers-that-be really have got it wrong. More and more, I have been invited to give lectures in a whole variety of venues and countries, from book festivals and farmers' meetings to university research departments, all over Britain from

Shetland to Cornwall and from China to New Zealand to Brazil, and learnt a great deal from everyone I have met—it's a good way to become aware of all (or at least a great range of) the possible arguments.

This book is a summary of thoughts so far—on what's gone wrong and why, and how to put things right. I wanted to make it as short as possible, preferably to be read in a couple of hours or less, though it has grown a bit. Maureen Doolan and Eleanor Peat at the Pari Center for New Learning, Tuscany, have provided the opportunity, through their company, Pari Publishing. I am very grateful to them and to Andrea Barbieri for his excellent design.

But most of all I am indebted to my wife, Ruth; and to my children, Amanda, Amy, and Robin, and their husbands and wife—Andrew, Julian, and Dawn—and my granddaughters, Amelie, Hazel, Ella, and Lottie, for demonstrating first hand that the world will not end when I do.

CHAPTER I

Good food for everyone forever —but only if we take matters into our own hands

The message of this book is as positive as anyone could hope for: the future could still be glorious. We just have to do things differently.

But by 'We', I mean people at large. 'We'—ordinary citizens, known to the powers-that-be as 'the public', to be gulled, cajoled, and ultimately blamed—have to take matters into our own hands. The powers-that-be—governments, the corporates, and the intellectuals and experts who are paid to tell them what they want to hear—are screwing things up horribly, and seem more or less bound to go on doing so. So the task is complicated because for the time being we will have to work around the people and the institutions who affect to be in charge but in truth are getting in the way.

To be sure, on the face of things, our present position could hardly be worse. At least forty years ago the 'Greens' began to warn of pending disaster, and now everyone is doing it. Britain's Archbishop of Canterbury Dr Rowan Williams has talked of mass wipe-out— two billion deaths from global warming—while the President of Britain's Royal Society, Lord (Martin) Rees, suggests that our civilization has only a 50-50 chance of survival, at least in a tolerable state, beyond the present century.

The excuse from on high is that the task has simply become too difficult. There are, we are told, too many of us. In addition, we are beset by forces that are beyond all control: earthquakes, tsunamis, failed monsoons. But the powers-that-be are doing the best that can be done. Their solution is for more of the same: more science, more cash, more control of natural phenomena and of people: no more 'failed states'; an end to 'terrorism'. The world's most powerful governments, the corporates who provide the money, and the experts and intellectuals who are paid to advise them, are on the case. All will be well. Never fear. Or if it isn't, then be assured that things could have been even worse (although it isn't at all clear what could be worse than mass annihilation).

Yet the truth is almost entirely opposite. We are not suffering because there are too many of us. Ours is a restless planet and tsunamis and the rest don't help—but our world is eminently habitable nonetheless. The cause of all our troubles has almost nothing to do with the difficulties that nature presents us with. The fault lies almost entirely with policy and strategy: ideas and courses of action dreamed up by human beings and put into practice by human beings. If we, humanity, analyzed our own problems more astutely and from first principles, and if we did things differently, then even at this late hour we could create a world that was good for everyone, and for all our fellow creatures, forever. We should certainly be thinking of the next 10,000 years, or indeed of the next million. There is no good biological reason why our species should not last for at least that long. That we should be seriously doubting our ability to make the world safe even for our own grandchildren is ludicrous.

I am going to focus on the world's food supply, 'from farm to fork' as the cliché has it. Food is not the only thing we have to get right—of course not; for everything is connected with everything else. But food is the most pressing issue—day by day and even hour by hour: the thing we absolutely have to get right. Get farming right, and everything else we want to achieve can begin to fall into place, from the day-to-day pleasures of good eating and social living, to the grand aspirations of full and fulfilled employment, world peace, and the conservation of wildlife. Get agriculture wrong, and everything else is compromised. At present, of all human endeavours, farming is the most ill-fashioned and ill-starred of all, and the ill effects of this are indeed felt everywhere, and by everyone; and the solutions proposed and put in train by the powers-that-be are making things worse.

To begin with, though—just to get the negatives out of the way—are things really as bad as they seem? To which, regrettably, the answer is 'Yes'—and probably far worse; although, through the gloom, there are a few rays of sunlight—enough to give serious grounds for hope.

The bad news

First, the world population now stands at 6.8 billion (6800 million). China and India between them account for 40 per cent of the whole, with more than 1.3 billion in China, and 1.2 billion in India. Then there are about a billion in Africa, 710 million in Europe, 514 million in the continent of North America, around 380 million in South America, and 143 million in Russia. The world total is just over twice what it was in 1950, four times greater than in 1900, six times more than in 1800, and somewhere between 200 and 600 times more than at the time of Christ. That, we hardly need telling, is a lot. But numbers continue to grow. By 2050, so the United Nations tells us, there will be nine billion of us.

Of the 6.8 billion who are with us now, so the UN surmises, roughly one million are chronically undernourished. Many simply don't have enough to eat and some suffer from specific deficiencies—like the estimated 40,000 children who are blinded each year through deficiency of vitamin A. Yet at the same time another billion suffer from the modern phenomenon of overnourishment. Obesity in many communities is the norm—and not simply, or even usually, among rich people. It's the poorer people who are fatter these days—you see fat kids in Brazil and China and among black and poor white South Africans, sometimes in the same neighbourhoods where other kids are seriously underfed. It all depends what side of the burger-and-soda line you are on. Obesity *per se* is not outstandingly dangerous—but it is associated with conditions that are; such as coronary heart disease (CHD) and diabetes. CHD now accounts for an astonishing 30 per cent of all deaths worldwide: 15 million per year, including 11 million in the 'developing' world. Soon, according to the World Health Organization, the number of diabetics worldwide could exceed the total population of the present United States.

Then again, an estimated one billion people worldwide—at least one in seven of all of us—now live in urban slums. Yet the cities continue to grow—with many countries actively pursuing policies of urbanization. The Chinese estimate that within the next few decades another half billion people will abandon the countryside for the cities—roughly the total population of the newly expanded European Union; and these will be *additional* to the people who already live in China's cities. For the first time, in 2006, the number in cities worldwide equalled the number in the countryside. By 2050, on present trends, two-thirds of all humanity will live in cities: the number of city-dwellers will approach the total population of the present world. The population of Mexico City and a few others is already around 20 million. By 2050, on present trends, some will have reached 50 million, equal to the total population of present-day England. If the cities could cope, then that would be fine. City life can be highly agreeable. Already, however, it is clear that the cities cannot keep up. In the Third World in particular all the big cities are surrounded and interlaced by slums—shanties, favelas—and parts of many if not most big cities of the west are exceedingly unpleasant to live in, and often seriously dangerous (and again, the 'improvements' imposed from on high over the past half century have often made things worse).

Alongside the rising numbers is rising consumption. Indeed, people in poor countries become very angry, and justifiably, when people who live in rich countries lecture them. As the Californian environmentalist Paul Ehrlich has been pointing out for more than three decades, an impeccably demographic middle-class family in Los Angeles, with Mom, Pop, and two bouncing kids, reading respectively for law and medicine and therefore of unquestionable value to humankind, consumes more than an entire Bangladeshi village. The US has only four per cent of the world's population and yet consumes more than a fifth of all the world's energy, and the same is roughly true of resources as a whole. The British are well behind middle-class Americans in the consumption stakes, but even so it would require the resources of three planets Earth to 'raise' everyone to the material standards of the average Brit. For all of us to live at the standards of rich Californians would require—well, an infinity of Earths; for there is no obvious upper limit to what people can consume if they put their minds to it.

Because of this—ever-increasing consumption, rather than mere numbers—the world's most basic resources on which all depends are seriously compromised. In 1999 the United Nations Environment Programme concluded that the lack of fresh water was second only to global warming in the league table of threats. One person in five at present has no access to water fit to drink—yet demand is liable to increase by 40 per cent over the next two decades. Less than three per cent of the world's water is fresh, and two-thirds of that is locked up in ice (although it is melting rapidly, though mostly in places that are more or less out of reach of humankind). Crops and livestock are especially thirsty: about 70 times more fresh water is needed to provide one person with their daily 3000 or so kcals of energy than they need for washing and so on. The next wars, so many sober analysts suggest, may well be fought over fresh water.

Land is at a premium, too. The total world area is just under 150 million square kilometres. About a third of the whole is Asia, another fifth is Africa, a sixth is North America and another eighth is South America. Europe accounts for about one-fifteenth of the whole, and Australia is just a bit smaller than Europe. About a third of all the world's land—around 50 million square kilometres—is farmed: the area cultivated or grazed has increased five-fold over the past 300 years. So now there are about 120 people for every square kilometre of farmland. Agriculture continues to spread— only about 45 million square kilometres were farmed in 1966—but we are getting to the end: most of what isn't farmed these days is desert, mountain, or city. But in 2006 the International Food Policy Research Institute (IFPRI) reported that about 40 per cent of all the world's farmland is already seriously degraded. As global warming bites and sea-levels rise the world's coastal strips, where much of the most productive farming is carried out, will disappear.

Oil, as all the world knows, is a finite resource that must run out eventually and, so many say, the 'tipping point' could some in the next decade or so—or may already be passed. The tipping point, roughly speaking, is the half-way point, when it is no longer possible to go on increasing the supply: when there are no more big fields still to be found, and it becomes obvious that we are simply working through what's left. There are fossil fuel alternatives—coal, natural gas, and the huge beds of shale oil (oil locked fairly tightly into rock) that underlie North America. In general, we extract the more accessible oil first. As we get towards the end we have to expend more and more energy to get out and process whatever remains. If we burn what's left too quickly we will load more carbon dioxide into the atmosphere than the world's rocks, plankton, and plants can absorb, and so the CO^2 concentration will increase, and so the world as a whole will grow warmer and warmer, and the seas grow deeper as the ice melts on Greenland and Antarctica. Yet modern economies and ways of life are geared to oil—more and more and more of it—to the point of almost complete dependence. Sixty per cent of Americans live in suburbs where life is impossible without a car; many drive 20 miles each way to the office, and 30 miles to take their dog to the vet. Skyscrapers that are the pride of modern cities are useless without elevators that are powered by electricity which for the most part is generated by oil. Without oil, or a very convincing substitute, most of America's most valued real estate becomes so much junk; badly located rubble.

The modern food supply chain uses a great deal of oil. The US uses 20 to 30 times more energy per head than the Third World does, and almost a fifth of the US uptake is used for food: the US expends more fuel energy on food than France uses for all purposes. Only one-fifth of the US uptake is for growing crops; the rest is for packaging, transport, and storage. Of all the energy used for growing food, in the US and in the world in general, nearly a third is used to make artificial fertilizers while another third runs the tractors and combines. The rest is for irrigation (7 per cent in the world as a whole, 13 per cent in the US), pesticides, and so on. The industrialization of agriculture, US-style, is widely perceived as a prime indication of 'progress'; already, worldwide, 95 per cent of all food production depends on oil. Traditional, labour-intensive farming has become a source of shame. Of course fossil fuels aren't the only source of energy. But nothing that is on the horizon will ever be as cheap and easy as oil has been. The biggest party in the history of planet Earth is all but over. This alone is enough to suggest that if we seriously want to feed the world's people, we have to change direction.

While all this is going on, power is shifting from the West—basically the United States and Europe, with noises off from Australia—to the East: mainly to China and India. For instance—just to take one rather stark statistic: in the mid-1990s the US retailers Wal-Mart got 94 per cent of its products from within the US but now, 80 per cent of the suppliers on its database are Chinese. The 'tiger economies' as in Japan and Malaysia have a curiously hybrid status, betwixt and between. Russia will soon be rich again from all its oil and gas—not happy, for it seems to have little gift for happiness—but rich. Right now Russia is sitting on the fence, cosy with the Chinese, anxious not to offend the US.

Britain has kept up the illusion of prosperity these past few decades by a series of con tricks. For the time being China in particular is flooding the world with goods that are extremely cheap, mainly because it has been paying its own workers extremely low wages, currently averaging $4600 per year. At the same time, Eastern Europe remains a source of cheap labour, and so too are the poor countries of Britain's former Empire, notably India and Pakistan. Brazil, too, is now exporting cheap labour. Successive British governments since the early days of Margaret Thatcher in the late 1970s, ever eager to cash in on short-term bonanzas, always strong on rhetoric but almost bereft of foresight, have run down Britain's industries partly because British workers have tended to be stroppy and hard to deal with, but also because, for the time being, it has been cheaper to buy goods and labour from abroad than at home. Britain's big and valuable coalmines were run down in the 1980s and until very recently a great many senior politicians and civil servants would have liked to dispense with agriculture too, although few had the courage to say so openly. To be sure, there seems to have been some change of heart. At the Oxford Food Conference in January 2010 Britain's Secretary of State for the environment and agriculture, Hilary Benn, said that Britain should start producing more of its own food. But, he was careful to add, only if we can produce it more cheaply at home than we could buy it in from Brazil.

Overall, this past few decades, Britain has been turning itself into a nation of hairdressers and money-changers while cashing in on its history and on the once-in-a-lifetime economic transition of China. For the time being, we seem to be richer than many other countries. But this apparent wealth is mostly an illusion. It depends largely on 'the city'—the historical fact that Britain has been a clearing house of other people's money and in the modern economy the exchange of money is the most lucrative pursuit of all, although it generates nothing of use except more money. We are temporarily well off too because we once had an Empire, and came out on the winning side in World War II and in the Cold War. Apart from all this, we now do very little that truly puts us out in front. This state of affairs, which depends almost entirely on what happened in the past, and to a significant extent on the distant past, cannot endure for much longer. China's transition is a one-off; and so, too, therefore is the flood of cheap goods that the rest of the world has been swallowing up. Chinese workers are already demanding better wages and soon their goods must go up in price. But Britain and other such countries will still be obliged to buy what China produces because we have given up making things for ourselves. Of course, too, the Chinese boom is not sustainable. Soon, they too will suffer from declining oil like everybody else. They are already suffering climate change, as the Gobi encroaches on Beijing, by 30 km a year. I have seen the maize dying on the outskirts of Beijing. The farmers know it is bound to die as the rains fail but they plant it anyway because that's what they do, and there is nothing else. When China declined in the past, the rest of the world cashed in. When it declines in the future, all the world will suffer.

The shift of power from West to East is not bad in itself. There is no good reason to suppose that the East will make a worse job of bossing the world than the West has done these past few hundred years. But the rise of the East will not be smooth and the West, particularly the US, will not go quietly. As Lord Rees points out, the chances of world conflict, as the superpowers scrabble for water, land, and particularly oil, and, more abstractly, for the status of top dog, are as great as they were at the height of the Cold War in the late 1950s, when we were all supposed to live in mortal fear of being blown to kingdom come. The US with Britain shamefully in tow seeks to distract attention from this horrendous threat and to rattle its sabres vicariously by focusing on terrorism and 'nuclear proliferation': the spurious threat from countries like Iraq, Iran and North Korea. In the same way, at the end of World War II, President Truman dropped the atom bomb on the Japanese mainly to frighten the Russians. But the true nature of American angst is obvious; and the issue is not that the Chinese are bad, and the US is good, or vice versa, but that both feel the need to be on top (and where Russia will stand in this pending struggle for commercial and military dominance has yet to be seen).

On top of all this, as even the world's politicians now seem to acknowledge, comes global warming. Predictions vary; indeed the most reliable prediction is that precise prediction is impossible. It is impossible to say whether any one place on Earth will become wetter or drier, hotter or colder. Britain is an extreme case: we could have Mediterranean climates in Scotland, with Scottish Shiraz competing with Scotch whiskey. Or the Gulf Stream that flows north from the tropics and keeps Britain warm could simply cease to flow, and then Britain would be as cold as Baffin Land. It seems likely though not certain that most of Africa will be arid, and possibly most of Brazil as well: the already dry forest of the Cerrado reduced to desert; the Amazon forest broken into scattered woods, as it probably was during warmer times in the past.

We can be sure only that we are in for a century or so of extremes, as the difference between the world's hot spots and cold spots increases: more violent hurricanes, more snow-bound winters, even hotter summers. It is clear, too, that ocean levels will rise as the ice-caps melt—perhaps by a metre by the end of the 21st century and perhaps, if the Greenland ice melts, by up to six metres in the fullness of time. A one metre rise will seriously encroach on the world's coastal strips, where half of all human beings live, and which include much of the world's most productive farmland. One metre will be enough to wipe out quite a few small island states, and seriously to embarrass many of the world's major cities, including London, New York, Amsterdam (and of course Venice). A six-metre rise would virtually wipe out Bangladesh, with a population that now approaches 200 million—more than Russia.

But long before we face such dramas we can be sure that many of the world's crops will start to fail. All modern crops live at their physiological limits. Change the conditions ever so slightly and they are likely to give up. It isn't just the changing temperature that can affect them. It's the new combinations of conditions—warm temperatures at times of shortening daylength, when they would normally expect the weather to be cold; unseasonal rainfall, too much or too little. A Canadian agriculturalist told me more than a decade ago that he fears for the Canadian wheat belt—and much of the world depends on the Canadian wheat crop. To be sure, it should often or even usually be possible to breed new crops to cope with novel conditions. But not if the conditions are too extreme. Even if they are not too extreme in principle, it takes at least a dozen years to produce a new variety that will yield reliably in new conditions—and then the seed has to be multiplied, and multiplied again, to provide enough to sow the world's vast fields. Crops can fail instantly. We may not have a dozen years to play with. Genetic engineering, for all the hype that has attended it, cannot and will not provide any instant fix. After a novel gene has been put into some existing crop plant it still takes years of selection to turn the receiving crop into something useful—assuming it really is useful—and to multiply the seed. Genetic engineering is just a technique. It is strategy and foresight that count—and they have gone seriously missing.

Yet the word seems to have got around that food is just a matter of money. Bob Geldof, rock musician turned saviour, recently opined that if the hungry people of Niger had money they could buy food. Well so they could, as things are at present. But they cannot buy food if there is none to buy. Neither can anybody else—not even Britain, for all its residual wealth. If there is food to be bought on the world market when global warming starts to bite, who will be able to out-bid the Chinese? As global warming bites there can be no guarantees that *anyone* will be able to eat. Common sense suggests that in times of such uncertainty it would be prudent to grow crops everywhere where they can be grown at all, in the hope and expectation that at least some of them will do well (although we cannot predict which ones); and it makes sense, too, to grow as many different types of crop as possible—different species, and different varieties within species—so as to spread the risk. In general, in the face of great uncertainties, it is hard to improve on common sense. In reality, present-day policies are flying absolutely in the face of common sense, as we grow more and more of the same kinds of crop in greater and greater quantities in fewer and fewer places, as if the world will go on forever as it is now. The powers-that-be, it seems, do not read the newspapers or if they do, they prefer to live in their own dream-worlds, intent on the next election or 'the bottom line', taking advice from people who have a vested interest in the status quo, relying on institutions that have too much inertia to change direction. I will come back to all this.

So here, in brief, is the catalogue of present-day threats. We could throw in a few more—not the least of which is or are infections: AIDS; livestock-borne diseases such as BSE/ CJD, bird 'flu and swine 'flu; tuberculosis—an infection that thrives on poverty, malnutrition, and over-crowding; malaria, which is ever-present; and no doubt a continuing string of novelties (of which AIDS and BSE/CJD are two recent examples) as we inevitably increase our contact with wild creatures, and as existing pathogens mutate. But the broad power struggles of the world, the diminishing resources, climate change—and the effect that all of these are having on farming and hence on our food supply—are enough to be going on with.

So where is the good news—these 'rays of sunlight'?

The good news

Oddly enough, one good reason for hope lies in the matter—the very large matter—of human population.

For as Fred Pearce describes in his excellent new book *Peoplequake* (Transworld, London, 2010) when the world population reaches nine billion, round about 2050, it should stabilize. Nine billion should be the greatest number there will ever be. For the first time in 10,000 years—since farming first began on a large scale—the problem of feeding everybody can be seen to be finite. We, humanity, and the world at large, will no longer be feeding a population that seems destined to grow indefinitely. We, and the world at large, can heave a mighty sigh of relief. This, at least, is what the United Nations demographers are now telling us.

Populations grow when the birth rate exceeds the death rate—so much is obvious. Even the smallest excess, even in slow-breeding creatures like elephants and humans, produces a remarkable rise in numbers in a remarkably short time. If numbers grow by a trivial one per cent per year—a hundred individuals at the start of each year and a hundred-and-one at the end—then the population will double every 80 years. So it was that when human beings first began to farm on a significant scale, at the end of the last Ice Age, world numbers stood at an estimated 10 million. By the time of Christ, the world population was an estimated 100 to 300 million—a 10 to 30-fold increase, achieved over 8000 years. By 1800 AD world numbers reached 1000 million—one billion: a further three-fold increase in 1800 years. The population took another century to double again: two billion by 1900, the start of the 20th century. The next doubling, to four billion, was achieved by the 1970s—and the United Nations held its first World Food Conference in Rome in 1974.

So between the time of Christ and the 20th century numbers increased 20-fold. But that is not all that happened. Particularly after the agricultural and then the industrial revolutions of the 17th century onwards, the percentage rate of increase, increased: that is, the time that it took the population to double was steadily reduced. The percentage rate of increase reached its maximum in the 1960s—at around two per cent per year. Such a rate doubles the total in 40 years. So if numbers had continued to grow at the 1960s rate, we could have expected a population of around 8 billion by 2010, and 16 billion by 2050, and 32 billion by 2090, and 60-odd billion by about 2130, and 120 billion-plus by the end of the 22nd century. I have met agriculturalists who put somewhat too much faith in modern technology who suggest that the world could fairly easily sustain a world population of 20 billion. I have never met any who think that 30 billion would be sustainable. Yet that is the kind of figure that would have been reached within the lifetimes of our grandchildren, if 1960s rates had continued. One hundred billion—the number projected in our great-great grandchildren's time—is beyond fantasy.

If things had gone on in that vein then, frankly, I don't know what would have been our best strategy, moral or technical. Perhaps we should never give up. St Paul stressed that hope is one of the three prime virtues (along with faith and charity). But it is hard to envisage any course of action that would have been effective, or indeed acceptable. Draconian curtailment of our reproduction, or a lemming-like procession to collapse: a foul choice.

But it seems we have been spared all that. The percentage increase of growth has steadily diminished since the 1960s and by 2050 it should, on present trends, be down to zero. If the percentage increase is zero then, by definition, numbers stabilize. It will not be that easy to feed nine billion people well and forever—the title of my book exaggerates somewhat—but it should be well within our grasp. It should be eminently do-able, even in the face of global warming and diminishing oil. Given that it is do-able, and that the alternative must imply some kind of disaster, it would surely be seriously remiss not to give it a go.

There is a second serendipity. Intellectuals of many kinds have been worried about 'overpopulation' at least since the start of the 19th century when the English cleric Thomas Robert Malthus first suggested that while the human population was growing geometrically (by a proportionate increase each year), the food supply could increase only arithmetically (by a fixed amount each year). Sooner or later, he concluded, starvation must set in. Ebenezer Scrooge, created by Charles Dickens in 1843, spoke of 'the surplus population': surplus, that is, to what was needed to keep the new factories running, and surplus to what could readily be fed (within the context of mid-19th century agricultural policy). Throughout the 19th and 20th centuries many have defended and even welcomed war, epidemic, natural disaster and famine on the grounds that they reduced the numbers of people who would otherwise have starved anyway, and led others to starve as well.

It turns out, though, that war, pestilence, catastrophe and famine do not contain numbers effectively. Indeed, they don't work at all. Wars and epidemics can reduce numbers dramatically—but people bounce back after them. The Black Death of 14th century Europe reduced the population by a third, but it was only a blip on the demographic chart. Within a few centuries Europeans were overflowing, in particular into the Americas. A baby boom followed World War II. With a few exceptions, such as the rich, Catholic, Kennedy family, it is generally the people in the poorest and most desperate societies who have the biggest families—partly because they fear, rightly, that many of their children are liable to die; partly because children represent security in old age, in societies without pension schemes; and partly because, in many poor societies, women have no status at all except as mothers—and the more they multiply the more their kudos grows.

In reality, the birth rate goes down when people feel *more* secure; when they are not hungry; when their children are not liable to die; and when women have greater opportunities for personal fulfilment, apart from increasing the family. Technology helps a great deal of course—access to reliable contraception—but it seems significant that the country that was first to reduce its birth rate to below replacement level was Catholic Italy where, one might suppose, contraception would be frowned upon. Germany's population would now be falling if the Berlin wall had not come down, and brought in the East Germans. The only modern country that seems to buck the trend is Russia, whose population is falling even though its people are neither affluent nor contented. The Russians seem to have stopped breeding out of despair; but I know of no formal studies on the reasons for their falling birth rate, and should not speculate.

Overall, the picture is encouraging: that people have fewer children when things are going well; not when things are going badly. The changes that produce such a shift—security, affluence, opportunity—are the kind that would be entirely welcome on their own account. The effect on containing population is a bonus—but an enormous one.

In short: the measures needed to contain population and to give the human species a good chance of survival into the 22nd century and beyond are entirely benign. Cruelty and neglect are counterproductive. All this suggests, too, that when we human beings are just given a chance to live our lives as we would like, then we manage our affairs very well. It is only when people are stressed that things start to go wrong—or when they are coerced from above. The women in China who are now being ordered to have only one child are the daughters and granddaughters of women who were told, by Mao Zedong, to have as many babies as possible.

The final, huge reason for encouragement lies within the human race itself. At least within the western, Christian tradition, prophets, intellectuals of all kinds, and politicians have been queuing up to tell us what a bad lot we are. The Old Testament told us we are conceived and born in sin—a concept seized upon a few centuries after Christ by St Augustine, and developed in their different ways both by the Roman Catholics and, in the 16th century, by John Calvin. A key theme of the Enlightenment of 18th-century Europe was that human beings in a state of nature are basically savages in all the pejorative senses, all at each others' throats; and would continue to be so were it not for the soothing and smoothing hand of Civilization. Civilization in turn (it was taken to be self-evident) depended on the elite, intellectuals and born leaders, who alone could be relied upon to rescue the mob from its own venality. Disdain on the one hand; conceit on the other. This attitude persists. Politicians continue to wag their fingers at us as if we were all idiots and natural-born miscreants and in the apparent belief that they really do know better.

Charles Darwin, though himself a fine and humane liberal, who for example faced up to slave-owners on their own turf in South America, managed inadvertently to add fuel to the flames. In his seminal work of 1859, *On the Origin of Species by Means of Natural Selection*, he stressed the role of competition in shaping evolution. 'Survival of the fittest' is how the philosopher Herbert Spencer summarized natural selection, and Darwin himself later adopted the phrase. Various kinds of intellectuals and politicians were thus confirmed in their belief that they had risen to the top of society because they were innately superior—and that, being superior, they had a 'natural' right to bash the weak. Thus disdain, conceit, and solipsism had apparently been reinforced by science—which, as the 19th century gave way to the 20th, was taken to be synonymous with rationality, and therefore to be incontrovertible.

Many brave souls spoke out against all this, from Jean-Jacques Rousseau in the 18th century through various Romantic and Socialist movements in the 19th and 20th centuries, and writers, thinkers, and artists such as John Ruskin, William Morris, Mahatma Gandhi, and Ivan Illich. Between them they have pointed out that 'ordinary' human beings are actually rather brilliant. In every sphere—building, farming, fishing, milling, cooking, carpentry, metal-working, music-making, tanning, weaving—we find that the basic skills are immensely subtle, and so too is the understanding that goes with them. On the moral front, common experience tells us that people are not innately 'savage'. People at large simply do not need self-appointed proctors to tell them how to behave. So it was that on June 15 1944, after hiding in an attic for several years while the Nazis rampaged through Amsterdam, Anne Frank wrote in her diary: ' … in spite of everything I still believe people are really good at heart'. I am sure she was right: and right to keep her faith in humanity. Ordinary Germans weren't Nazis. Nazism was a flight of fancy, of politicians and intellectuals. The sin of ordinary people was to follow their leaders. Alas, it is a mortal sin. For my part, I have wandered into many a village in many a remote quarter of the world and only in one particular corner of Britain where the English are seen as the enemy have I been treated with less than courtesy. A particular village in India stands out in my memory where the head-man, who was about four feet tall and lived in a house of about the same height, insisted on introducing me and my companion to all of his seemingly endless family. In remotest Turkey my daughter and I bought tea in the village café—except that we weren't allowed to buy it, because we were ushered in as guests, and plied with honey cakes for good measure.

If most people are as nice, and sensible, as I believe is demonstrably (and theoretically) the case, then it seems to follow that if only the will of the people at large could prevail, then the world should be a much better place. It boils down to democracy: a central task, indeed the sine qua non, is to make democracy work.

You may feel this notion is simply a flight of fancy—but there is very good reason for thinking it is the case. First, as a matter of historical interest, Immanuel Kant in the late 18th century predicted that any nation that was truly democratic would never initiate war. Of course it would fight in its own defence when attacked, but if the people's will truly prevailed then the people would never choose to go to war unless they had to. Modern studies suggest that Kant was absolutely right. So it was that in the 1990s Professor Randolph J Rummel of the University of Hawaii examined 353 wars between pairs of nations between 1816 and 1991 and found that no two, true democracies had ever fought each other in all that time. Democracies had fought non-democracies, and non-democracies had fought each other, but democracies never make war on other democracies. (Rummel defined a 'democracy' as a state with universal suffrage and a free press, and a 'war' as any conflict that caused more than 1000 casualties, which all seems fair enough).

On the present issue—the world's food supply—the Nobel Prize-winning economist Amartya Sen has pointed out that famine simply does not occur in democracies. Full stop.

But we denizens of the western world should not be feeling complacent. As Thom Hartmann chillingly spells out in *What Would Jefferson Do?* (Three Rivers Press, New York, 2004) the United States and Britain have been rigorously undermining their own democracies this past 30 years, and particularly after the attack on the World Trade Centre on September 11, 2001. The governments have taken more and more power to themselves, systematically undermining rights that we used to consider fundamental, including rights of assembly. Demonstrably, too, both countries miserably fail the test of democracy proposed by the Austrian-British philosopher Karl Popper. The point is not, said Popper, how a society elects its own leaders, or even whether it elects them, but whether it can get rid of them when it decides that they no longer serve its interests. At the time that I wrote this chapter, only small minorities actively support Bush and Blair. By contrast, tribal chiefs often seem to have autocratic powers but (so many an anthropological study has shown) it usually turns out that if the chief once loses the trust of his people, then his reign ends instantly.

I may seem to digress somewhat. But my proposals for rescuing the world include the idea that democracy is key; the necessary changes can be brought about only by democratic means. It is good to have independent and scholarly support for the idea that democracy really does work—if we can only install it in the first place.

Craft, too, is a vital and related concept. Crafts evolve: they represent the collective skills and knowledge of entire societies. They are by their nature democratic. Agriculture as practiced through all but the last few decades of the past 10,000 years has been a craft industry. Modern commercial scientists and the companies that employ them like to give the impression and perhaps believe that the world's farming was in a dreadful mess until they came along, beginning in the late 19th century but particularly in the mid 20th, and rescued us.

Again, the truth is quite opposite. Modern agricultural science has succeeded insofar as it seems to have done only because it had thousands of years of traditional craft to work with. By the time modern science came on the scene, wild plants and animals had already been tamed and re-fashioned and the fields made ready— not by university departments and teams of corporate scientists but by ordinary farmers, tackling life's problems; and before them by hunters and gatherers, who had worked out what is edible and compliant and what is downright dangerous. At the other end of the food chain the world's great chefs rightly grow rich from their artistry—but the best of them emphasize that they build on tradition: that their core skills and their finest recipes were devised over centuries by 'ordinary' cooks in a hundred million kitchens, in Italy and Provence and Turkey and China and all the rest. The Medicis and the other great families of Renaissance Italy built Florence and Siena and all the other great and enviable cities amidst the fields of a peasant economy—but it was only because they left the peasants alone to get on with their work that the glorious civilization that we have inherited was able to arise at all.

In truth, too, Darwin's *Origin of Species* when properly understood does not predict that human beings should fight, all against all, unless otherwise restrained. All creatures depend on other creatures for their survival. All must cooperate as much as they compete. Social animals especially must emphasize cooperativeness—and human beings are more social than most. Human evolution, we should properly predict, is *bound* to produce sociality. Evolutionary theory predicts that most human beings, in any one society, are bound to be nice, because no society can hold together except by sociality and cooperativeness. Unfortunately, theory also predicts that nice people are bound to be dominated by nasty people: the minority who are more aggressive, and want to be out in front. There is the rub, the central dilemma of humankind. More of this later.

Meantime I want only to note this second outstanding reason for hope: that we can, in the end, trust ourselves. History, common experience, and evolutionary theory combine to tell us that we, people at large, are immensely ingenious and morally sound. We can take matters into our own hands. It is safe to do so.

So what, in practice, do we need to do? First, we need to get the moral philosophy right—to work out what we should be trying to do and why; and then we need to address the practicalities. I will look at the underlying philosophy in the next chapter. The practicalities occupy the rest of the book.

CHAPTER 2

Why should we give a damn?

The task before us—where 'us' means humanity—is to create a world that is good for 6.8 billion people now, and for 9 billion people by 2050, and for the estimated five to eight million other species with whom we share this Earth; and can go on catering for everyone and for other creatures forever—at least for the next 10,000 years, and preferably for the next million and beyond. That might not be possible, but it looks possible enough to be worth a try. The prize would be very great, while the price of failure exceeds our imagining. Technically, the task should be within our compass. So why don't we set about it?

One very strong reason is that a lot of people don't frame the problem in this way. Many don't agree that we, humanity, should be trying to cater for everybody, and for all other creatures. In practice, we don't need a majority to agree on what should be done, in order to make the necessary changes. Critical mass is what's needed. I know a great many who do agree that the world's task is to cater for everybody and there are surely enough in the world to do what needs doing—if only their thoughts and efforts could be coordinated.

But how could anyone disagree—that it is humanity's task to care for humanity, and the rest of the world where we all live? This is worth asking. It is useful to anticipate opposition.

How could anyone not give a damn?

Some—only a few, perhaps, but they are out there—just don't give a damn. 'Not my problem, mate', I have heard people say. Others do give a damn but seem too modest: 'Too much for my old head'—or as my maternal grandfather was wont to say, 'The government has got something up its sleeve, sonny, don't you worry about that!' Others agree with Voltaire, as in *Candide*: that every man should cultivate his own garden (and indeed, if more people did follow Voltaire's advice, including Britain and the US, the world would surely be a safer place). I was brought up in a Christian tradition and Christians take it for granted that where there is a moral wrong, then they should take it upon themselves to put it right. But Christ was more interventionist than most. Many believe that it is not morally proper to intervene unless specifically invited to do so. Some point out—with some justification—that you can never fully predict the effects of your actions, particularly when it comes to dealing with other human beings, so it is better not to interfere; just go with the flow. As the old proverb has it, 'The road to Hell is paved with good intentions'. Everybody hates a do-gooder. So there are all kinds of reasons for standing back and although some of them seem simply to be rooted in indifference and selfishness, others do have at least some forgivable caution behind them.

Others take a hard line. They positively, and sometimes adamantly, disagree that individual people *should* concern themselves with society as a whole, or with humanity as a whole. Some simply do not accept that cooperation is a positive force for good, or that society is more than a collection of solipsists, or that each individual should, in practice, make some concession to the whole. Compassion, they are inclined to argue, is namby-pamby, and ultimately destructive. Some appeal to Darwin (although Darwin would surely be turning in his grave): insisting that it is competition that leads to improvement, and that it is destructive to be generous to the losers, for that fosters weakness that in the end must destroy us all. Friedrich Nietzsche put a more high-sounding spin on this. He argued that God is dead, and therefore that the only judge of humankind is humankind. Among human beings, some prove to be superior—at least as judged by their own standards for there are, he insisted, no other standards by which to judge: and such people—*Ubermenschen*: 'overmen'; supermen—not only have a right, but a positive duty, to develop their own talents to the full, even though this may require them to ride rough-shod over the rest. Nietzsche did not invent the *Ubermensch* mentality, although I believe that he did coin the word. It is present in European imperialism, as we casually plundered the rest of the world—not in the Nietzschean belief that God was dead but with the conviction that because we were obviously superior to Africans and Asians and native Americans and Australians then we must be closer to God's image, so He would obviously be on our side. In modern times the US 'neoconservatives' who still dominate, openly parade their intention to reign forever in the guise of the world's only superpower; and those who get in the way are pushed aside. I know many Americans who are ashamed of this attitude bur have also met many others who simply accept that the neocon attitude is the way of the world.

In short: there are many, including some of the world's most powerful people, who for a whole raft of reasons do not agree that the task before humanity is to take care of all humanity, and of our fellow creatures. It isn't just that the scales have not yet fallen from their eyes. Some respectable philosophers have offered coherent reasons why universal compassion is positively offensive. They perceive it as a philosophy of weakness: ultimately destructive. Neither do you need to be an ardent atheist, as Nietzsche was, to espouse such views. Tony Blair and George W Bush, who created and perpetuated so much of what is wrong with the modern world, declared themselves to be Christians.

How do we know what's good?

But since there is more than one moral position to be taken, doesn't this prove the relativist argument, that there are no moral absolutes? I would like to argue this further—nothing is more important than the search for moral absolutes—but since this is not a book of moral philosophy I will make just a few quick points. First, despite the best efforts of some very fine philosophers such as Immanuel Kant, we cannot hope to discover or to define moral absolutes as if they were scientific laws. Kant's own suggestions (his 'categorical imperatives') in the end remain arbitrary. Many have posited that moral absolutes are what God says they are, by definition. But God's will is open to interpretation. Blair and Bush sought divine inspiration for all that they did, or so they told us.

Many realized by the end of the 18th century, hard on Kant's heels, that the search for moral absolutes was ultimately forlorn. Among them was England's Jeremy Bentham, who founded the modern school of 'utilitarianism', sometimes known more generally as 'consequentialism'. In utilitarian philosophy, actions are judged not by some absolute (but inevitably arbitrary) moral criterion, but according to their outcome. Human happiness was and is the goal, said the humanist Bentham: and the ideal is to achieve 'the greatest happiness of the greatest number'.

This seems straightforward enough, and utilitarianism has carried great weight. Yet there are serious problems with it. One is to define happiness, and to measure it. A modern solution to this problem is simply to equate happiness with wealth, on the grounds that it is better to be richer than poorer. So we find that ethical decisions are increasingly made on grounds of cost-effectiveness, or indeed of expediency. If such-and-such a course is more profitable, or easier, then it must be right. Consumerism is rooted in this philosophy: it is taken as read that people buy only those things that make them happy, and since happiness is the ultimate good, then whatever they are prepared to pay for must be good too. I have even heard human cloning justified in such terms. Guns, too: if guns make people happy, so the US gun lobby says, people should have guns; and if people make money out of making guns, then that is justification too. Yet, we might suggest, there are good and bad reasons for being happy. No one to my knowledge, at least in public, has defended child pornography on the grounds that it makes some people happy, or that it is profitable. You might say that utilitarianism covers this case since child pornographers are in the minority, so it isn't the greatest *number* who are made happy. But numbers don't carry the case either. If twelve Nazis beat up one gypsy, then twelve people are made happy and only one is miserable. In this instance, happiness far outweighs misery, at least if we simply count heads. Yet we feel that such beatings are foul, and that child pornography is foul. They are *wrong*. The true roots of morality, we might reasonably suppose, are not to be found in the happiness or the misery of individuals, but in the feelings that lead us to judge that some actions are acceptable, and some are not.

This leads us to yet another 18th century philosopher: David Hume. In the end, said Hume, morality can and must be guided by 'passion': emotional response; attitude. David Hume was at the hub of the Scottish Enlightenment—the ultimate rationalist—and yet, as a truly accomplished rationalist, he acknowledged the limits of what is commonly called rationalism. In the end, morality is a matter of feeling, and you have to go with your feelings. In the end we just have to state our moral positions in the way that Thomas Jefferson and his fellow authors did in 1776 when they framed the American Declaration of Independence: 'We hold these truths to be self-evident ...'. If only the US had stayed true to Jefferson the world would be a very different and better place. I do not presume to improve on Hume or on Jefferson. I will go with my feelings, as Hume recommended, and state, merely, that I take my conclusions in this matter to be self-evident, as Jefferson and his colleagues were content to do. It is right to cater for the whole human race. It is wrong to write people off, no matter how expedient this may be.

Two last words, however. First, if Hume is right—that morality is inevitably rooted in feeling—then it seems to me that if we truly want to refine our moral positions, we should set out deliberately to cultivate our emotional responses. This takes us into the realms of 'virtue ethics': ethics based not on absolutes or on cost-effectiveness—who gains, who loses, insofar as these things can be measured—but on attitudes. The moralists who over the past few thousand years have focused on essential attitudes include philosophers such as Aristotle and Lao Tzu. But in the main, it has not been the philosophers, but the prophets, who have stressed the need to approach life's moral problems in the right frame of mind. Atheists and other detractors are wont to argue that the prophets of different religions all pull in different directions—that what is acceptable to a Christian is taboo to a Moslem, and so on. But, invariably, the differences the detractors point to are merely matters of customs and manners—who eats pork or beef and who doesn't. At the deepest level, where morality truly begins, all the great religions are in agreement. The Ten Commandments of Moses urge us to *love* God, and *honour* our parents. Buddha spoke of compassion. Christ urged universal love. Mohammed spoke of justice and generosity. Hindus tend to be eclectic, and the 19th century Hindu mystic Ramakrishna summarized them all when he suggested that the moral position of all the great religions and their prophets can be encapsulated in three irreducibly simple phrases: personal humility; respect for fellow, sentient creatures; and reverence for God (although atheists may prefer to substitute 'nature' for 'God'). The point, as I see it, is that the pronouncements of the prophets are rooted firmly in metaphysics: in a notion of how the universe really *is*, and why it is right and proper to treat the world as a whole with reverence and other creatures, including other human creatures, with respect. But metaphysics, alas, has gone missing from modern western thinking, and certainly from modern political and economic thinking.

That's it. It is remarkable how many of today's most Gordian issues, even of the most technical and modern kind, seem to unravel when exposed to such simple, ancient wisdom. Still, I do not want to argue that what the world's great prophets have agreed upon is *ipso facto* correct and incontrovertible. But I do like the idea that what they have said, to a significant extent summarizes the deep morality of all humankind. The prophets are expressing what most of us feel deep down really is *right*; and they lived in ways that most of us, deep down, would like to be capable of. Of course (the detractors will say) there have been many prophets, and they did not all agree with the founders of the world's principal religions. Indeed. But I suggest that natural selection applies. The prophets who spoke of compassion—humility, respect, and reverence—are the ones we remember precisely because what they say chimes so precisely with our deepest convictions. They express not simply what we believe, but what we are. The prophets with different teachings have fallen by the wayside. The fans of Nietzsche are in the minority.

New light is thrown on all these discussions by game theory.

Game theory, and why nasty people are in charge

Ethics—morality—is in the end a matter of interaction: how creatures that are capable of making a choice, meaning human beings, treat third parties of their own species, or other species, or indeed the world in general. All discussion of any kind of interaction—war, commerce, ecology, evolution, or human societies in general—can be assessed, and indeed quantified, in terms of game theory. We can show by means of mathematical models, obligingly run by computers with standard software, what kind of behaviour is likely to bring greatest benefit, and to whom; and since the way we behave depends to a significant extent on our underlying beliefs and attitudes, game theory offers at last some insight into different moral philosophies.

One of the simplest of all game theory models is hawks versus doves. Hawks may be seen either as gangsters who simply don't give a damn, or as Nietzscheans who present coherent and high-sounding reasons for bossing everybody else around; and doves are people of the kind the prophets would approve of—humble souls, considerate of each others' feelings, anxious where possible to cooperate.

Game theory shows that societies composed entirely of hawks, collapse. The hawks spend all their time fighting for top-dog status, and beat each other up. But Bentham's ideal—the greatest happiness of the greatest number is achieved by all-dove societies, who waste no time at all in fighting and who, by cooperating, achieve far more for their common benefit than any could achieve alone. In practice, the all-dove society cannot be achieved except by adopting dovish attitudes.

But although the all-dove society is by far the best, the theory shows that it is not stable. It is bound to be invaded by hawks, for whom the doves provide easy pickings. The hawks can take what they like in an all-dove society, without fear of reprisal. The hawks may either invade from outside—some rival tribe or nation, in human terms—or arise from within, as some of the erstwhile doves discover that hawkishness offers an easy option.

The hawks, then, being very successful, soon increase. But the theory then takes another turn. For as the number of hawks increases, so they start to get in each other's way. A hawk swaggers in to what he takes to be a party of doves, demanding booty, and finds that some other hawk has already beaten him to it. So he gets in a fight. Thus (the theory has it) the number of hawks in any given society is self-limiting. When the proportion of hawks reaches, say, 20 per cent, it no longer pays to be a hawk. Hawkishness lands you in too many fights. When surrounded by too many hawks it is better to be a dove—even a reluctant dove: go with the flow, keep your head down, and stay out of trouble.

I find this simplest of models most illuminating. It predicts that if societies are left to themselves they finish up not with all-hawks, or with all-doves, but with a mixture of doves and hawks. Furthermore, the doves will greatly outnumber the hawks. The theory predicts, in short, that most individuals in any society that is left to itself are bound to be nice: cooperative and pacific. But the hawks will dominate even though they are the minority, precisely because they are hawks; and the doves don't want to fight back.

Doesn't this precisely describe what happens in human societies? Most people are nice, which is what I have been arguing all along. But in any one society the nice majority is bound to be ruled by people who simply want to rule. So it is that nice people usually find themselves dominated by nasty people. The Enlightenment notion that human beings are basically bad and need to be bossed by firm leaders is the precise opposite of the truth. Most people are basically nice while their leaders very often turn out to be gangsters. It seems to follow that if we, humanity, could only create true democracies—societies that truly reflected the will of the people—then the result should be most agreeable, because most people are doves, and doves are nice. But it is extremely difficult to establish true democracies because doves are inevitably dominated by hawks. We finish up with the kind of 'democracy' that we see in modern-day Britain or the US, where the masses of doves are allowed, at long intervals, to choose their leaders from a shortlist of hawks, each of whom they may find equally unsavoury. How can we create democracy, then? How can doves create societies dominated by doves when doves have no taste for domination? That is the central paradox and dilemma of humankind. I will address it in the last chapter.

Meanwhile, in lieu of true democracy, the powers-that-be are convinced that it is their right and destiny to rule, and the intellectual elite whom they employ are convinced that they alone know how to do things. In truth, the leaders are liable to be gangsters, while their compliant intellectuals to a significant extent emerge as *idiots savants*. The real genius, moral and practical, lies with humanity at large. The future lies with what that other great Enlightenment moralist, Adam Smith, called 'human sympathy'; and it lies, as philosophers from John Ruskin to Ivan Illich have argued this past few hundred years, with craft: the skills that have evolved among humanity at large. Since food is the thing we absolutely have to get right, the most important crafts are those of farming and cooking.

One final caveat, however. I know that many will be gnashing their teeth at this point, if they can bear to have read this far; and quite rightly. For I have met many people in high places who definitely are not gangsters, and agree absolutely that it is the proper and principal task of humanity to look after humanity. Some of them are Christians, some are Muslims, some Jews, some atheists. No matter: the common thread of human sympathy runs through all of them. But they disagree ardently with my general thesis—that the world needs re-thinking from first principles, and that humanity should put its trust in humanity at large. To be sure the present world is flawed, these critics say, but there is nothing fundamentally wrong with present-day technologies, or political or commercial institutions. Specifically, modern farming in its industrialized and high-tech form is good and necessary. The corporate food processors and supermarkets can feed the world much better than anybody else could do. All the infrastructure of modern technology and commerce are therefore necessary too—the science, the economic theory, the ever-tighter organization. The status quo doesn't need re-thinking. It just needs to be given a chance. As *The Economist* magazine declared on a recent cover (November 5 - 11, 2005): 'Tired of globalization but in need of much more of it'. We are in a period of transition. Just have patience.

These caveats are serious. I believe that some people who disagree with me are demonstrably wicked but I also know that some at least of my critics are hugely intelligent and at least as well-intentioned as I can claim to be. So I want to take this last class of criticisms seriously. But I will do this in later chapters. First I want to present my own thesis: that the task is to make a world that is good for everyone forever; that to do this we need to think again from first principles; and that we must focus, above all, on the food supply chain—which means on farming and cooking.

CHAPTER 3

Great food and enlightened agriculture: the future belongs to the gourmet

The task before us is to provide good food for everyone, forever; at the same time to create agreeable ways of life for farmers, and for everyone else involved in the food chain—and indeed for all humanity; to do this without cruelty to livestock; and to ensure that the world as a whole remains beautiful and secure, and that as many as possible of all the other species with whom we share this planet continue to thrive and to evolve. Farming is the key to all this—or at least it is the thing we really have to get right. It is the source of the thing that we need in greatest quantities, and without interruption; and it is the principal area of contact between humanity and the fabric of the Earth itself. The kind of farming that would do all that is necessary I call 'Enlightened Agriculture'.

'Enlightened' is a high-fallutin' term, with overtones both of the 18th century Enlightenment of Europe, with its emphasis on reason, and on the Buddhists' spiritual path. But because 'Enlightened Agriculture' sounds high-fallutin', and contains seven syllables, I have shortened it for PR purposes to 'Real Farming' (which only has three); and from now on will use the two expressions interchangeably. But whatever term we adopt, the concept is irreducibly simple. Enlightened Agriculture aka Real Farming is farming that is expressly designed to feed people, well and forever, without wrecking the rest of the world. Technically, it should be straightforward, too:

common sense and craft within a framework of sound biology. This is why I called my previous book on food and farming, 'Feeding people is easy'.

'Sound biology' means to acknowledge what ought to be most obvious: that human beings are flesh and blood creatures—that we are indeed animals, with the same fundamental needs as other animals; and that the world in which we live is our habitat. So it is an exercise in physiology, for we have to have some feel for what our own bodies need; and it is an exercise in psychology—for we need to respect our own desires; and in ecology—for we have to know the limits of the world itself, what it can do and what it cannot. At bottom we need primarily to regard ourselves as we really are—as a biological species with in-built physical needs like any other. Like any other species, too, we must avoid fouling our own nest.

All this should be too obvious to be worth saying yet it is totally at odds—*totally* at odds—with the thinking that has underpinned agricultural strategy in the western world over the past few centuries and in particular over the past few decades. It seems as if people in high places—including many 'leading' scientists, to their shame—like to nurse the effete conceit that human beings dwell in an ethereal, spiritual-cerebral world, or should aspire to do so; and the myth that began with Francis Bacon, that 'Man', meaning us, can 'conquer' nature and make the world do anything we want it to, for our own comfort; in other words, that we are *above* mere nature. As if as the *coup de grâce,* modern policy-makers have now fallen hook, line, and sinker for neoliberal economics and finance capitalism. Neoliberalism is vaunted as the 'global free market' and is supposed to solve all our problems and to be ultimately democratic. In reality, and inevitably, the 'free market' is dominated by the strongest players—the corporates; supported by governments, such as those of Britain and the US, which survive by supporting these corporates. 'Finance capitalism' means that money itself is treated as a commodity—not simply, as is its proper role, as a tool to facilitate trade and to keep score. As if to ensure disaster, the whole caboodle is supposed to be maximally competitive, in the vague (and it really is vague) belief that 'competition' leads to 'efficiency'; and this is taken self-evidently to be good—not least because it is conceived to be Darwinian and therefore 'natural'. In truth the modern market is not maximally competitive precisely because it is controlled by a few big players, but even if it was it would be a poor strategy since it is obvious to all who care to think about it, and know any history, that human beings and indeed all creatures achieve far more by cooperating than they can by fighting each other.

Be that as it may, the modern economy is conceived as a global dogfight—a to-the-death struggle for the maximum wealth (for nothing counts but money) in the shortest time. By some magical mechanism, more fantastical than any primitive, cultish myth, this mêlée is supposed to produce a tolerable world. Obviously it does not; and the reasons it does not are obvious too. Nonetheless, the modern powers-that-be—scientists, economists, politicians—subscribe to the myth. All human activity is forced into the neoliberal straitjacket. For some enterprises, perhaps, the damage is minimal. For most, and for most people, the present economy is very damaging indeed. For agriculture, which means for all humanity and all the world, it is a disaster that is possibly of terminal proportions. Unless we put the world economy back on a sound footing—which means the end of neoliberalism and of finance capitalism—then everything else we might try to do to make the world a better place, is doomed. Yet, as I will argue later, we do not need a Marxist revolution. We merely need to return to the kind of common-sense capitalism that was described and acted upon by the founders of the modern United States, Thomas Jefferson et. al., and which lies behind the essentially commonsensical, humanitarian economic philosophy of John Maynard Keynes, which set the tone for more or less all western countries in the decades before the 1970s.

I am primarily educated in science and feel that the present role of science in all this nonsense is shameful. The scientists who want to be employed these days are obliged to tell the powers-that-be what they want to hear—which is that with more high technology, it will be possible to reconcile the dream of maximum wealth with their stated, pious desire for a better world; and that with even more technology, it will be possible to reverse the damage done by the rampant exploitation of the world's resources that neoliberal competitiveness demands. This is either a giant and horrible lie, or a giant and horrible mistake. The mistake lies in a cardinal sin of philosophy, which is to imagine that omniscience and hence total control are within human grasp—so that we, human beings, can do anything we set our minds on, and dig ourselves out of any hole we dig ourselves into. This is simply wrong. It misconstrues the nature of the world and the nature of science. But the arrogance is stupendous.

In truth, agriculture has very rarely been designed expressly to feed people, and to my knowledge—apart from the modern organic movement—it has never expressly acknowledged the need to work within the bounds of sound biology, although this has sometimes been implicit. Most agriculture in the history of the world has been designed primarily to match and support the prevailing economic and political structure and beliefs of the day. This is equally evident in the open-field strips of Feudal Europe, or in England's great neo-Feudal proto-capitalist estates of the 18th century, or America's prairie homesteads, based on Thomas Jefferson's vision of the United States as 'a nation of small farmers', or in Stalin's collectivist farms of the 1930s and beyond.

But never in all history have the powers-that-be had the wherewithal to operate on the global scale as they do now. Never have they been able, as now, to take the whole of world farming by the scruff of its neck and ram it so procrusteanly into a structure and a philosophy that are so alien to its purpose, and so at odds with the needs of humanity and the biological and physical constraints of the world. The powers-that-be behave as if they were playing a game—which indeed they are: a game of money and power. They are forever lecturing protestors like me about the need to be 'realistic'; but the only reality they recognize is the commercial-military power game that they happen to be engaged in, and makes them rich. They have no feel at all for the physical realities of the world itself, and the creatures within it, and for the ways in which farming has, in reality, been practiced this past ten thousand years, and by whom. They have a great deal of 'data', which they collect and publish selectively, and manipulate with the aid of lawyers and other rhetoricians this way and that, largely for our bamboozlement, but that is not the same thing at all. The world is suffering, possibly terminally, from a huge irony: that the powers-that-be live in a fantasy world of their own devising, blind to every observation that is in any way inconvenient, yet they believe that they really do know what they are doing, and that they alone are the realists. We are dying of their illusions.

We (humanity) must now take matters into our own hands—and, I believe, it is well within our power to do so. We need to start again from first principles—and begin with three basic questions: 'What is necessary? What is possible?' and 'What is right?'. The last of these questions, obviously, is a matter of moral philosophy—and the answer is already implicit in the title of this book: it is to provide good food for everyone forever without wrecking the rest of the world. The first two questions are matters of biology. So, first, what is *necessary*? What do we need to grow if we are to feed ourselves well—and how much of it?

A lightning course in nutrition

Living bodies are complicated and it takes energy to keep them together. Food provides us with the raw materials from which to construct our own flesh and with the necessary energy, expressed as 'calories' (or more usefully as 'kilocalories' or kcals: each kcal is a thousand calories). It also, vitally, supplies a miscellany of bits and pieces which, broadly speaking, oil the works (for example acting as intermediaries in various metabolic pathways). The components of food that meet all these requirements are roughly classed as carbohydrates, fats, and proteins, which can be called 'macronutrients'; plus a very mixed bag of minerals, vitamins, and other recondite organic molecules, which are known collectively as 'micronutrients'.

Carbohydrates, in rock-bottom terms, are composed exclusively of just three chemical elements: carbon, hydrogen, and oxygen. In their simplest form carbohydrates manifest as sugars. Sugars joined together form 'polysaccharides' which take many forms.

Very common polysaccharides in nature include starch, which most plants create as a personal food-store, especially in seeds and tubers; glycogen, which animals create as a short-term source of energy, mostly stored in the muscles; and cellulose and various hemicelluloses, which form the tough but flexible cell walls of plants.

Broadly speaking, human beings need between 1500 and 4000 kcals per day depending on whether they are children or adults, growing or not growing, men or women, lactating or pregnant or neither, sedentary or sweat-of-the-brow labourers, and also on whether they naturally metabolize rapidly or less rapidly. Considering the enormous range of human sizes, shapes, and conditions, the total range of energy we require is surprisingly small—largely because big people need less energy weight-for-weight than small people, and so tend to be more economical. (This is for simple reasons of physics. Warm-blooded creatures like us use most of our energy creating body heat. Little bodies cool quicker than big bodies, whether the body in question is a human, an elephant, or a cup of coffee. So big bodies, weight for weight, are easier to keep warm and so are more economical). In most human diets (with a very few exceptions as in the traditional Inuit), carbohydrates are the chief source of energy. Whether in the form of simple sugars or of polysaccharides, carbohydrates provide roughly 420 kcals per 100 grams; so an average person (if there is such a thing!) could get all his/her daily energy needs from about 500-700 grams of carbohydrates, which is about a pound to a pound-and-a-half.

The chief carbohydrate by far in a traditional diet is starch—found mainly in the seeds and tubers of plants. Plants, then, in traditional diets, are our prime source of energy. However, human beings cannot digest cellulose (or at least, only to a very limited extent with the aid of bacteria in the hind gut); so cellulose and the hemicelluloses do not provide us with energy and old-style nutritionists were apt simply to dismiss them as 'roughage'. But, roughly beginning in the early 1970s, nutritionists have come to appreciate that so-called 'roughage' is an extremely important component of diet even though it provides virtually no calories. In particular, we now know that the colon isn't just a conduit but is an extremely important organ of absorption and (with the aid of gut bacteria) carries out some significant biochemistry. The presence or absence of roughage, and the physico-chemical details of it, have a great (if still largely unknown) influence on colon physiology, which in turn affects the body as a whole in many ways. In line with its new-found status, roughage is now called 'dietary fibre'. Carbohydrate in pure form, as in pure sugars or starch, is said to be 'refined'. Carbohydrate served up as it was in the original plant, with all the original fibre present, as in wholemeal bread, is said to be 'unrefined'.

Since human beings do not digest fibre to any appreciable extent, it increases the bulk of food without increasing the calories; and it is thereby said to 'dilute' the overall energy content. Since there is a limit to the amount that people can eat—or indeed are prepared to eat—fibre thus helps to limit total intake. Indeed it may be the greatest 'slimming' food of all. Indeed, some people in poor countries sometimes find that their diet is too fibrous. Women in many African villagers live almost exclusively on porridge made from maize or sorghum and may find it almost impossible to consume enough calories in a day to sustain a pregnancy or a lactation (which requires even more energy than pregnancy). Their children, too, newly weaned, may find that the calories in the local porridge are just too dilute. People on such diets need more concentrated food, rather than less. In this, poor people on diets that are very high in unrefined carbohydrates, and western people who ply themselves with sugars and fats, are mirror images of each other: the poor could do with less dilution, the rich with more.

The word 'dilution' could cause confusion since in most contexts 'diluting' means adding water. Indeed, water also adds bulk to a diet without increasing the energy content, but its overall effect on intake seems to be ambiguous. For instance, it is probably harder to slurp a lot of watery soup than to wolf a smaller amount of more concentrated stew. But sweet drinks are another matter. It is possible to drink gallons of what Americans call soda and the British traditionally called pop, without suppressing appetite at all, and thus take in several thousand calories a day in passing—literally. These days, many people do this. Pop is a comfort food, and habit-forming, not to say addictive (especially as some forms are rich in caffeine). It takes away some of the pain of the big hot noisy city, and of the air-conditioned office. Grossly obese people worldwide are typically pop-swiggers. Thus, white sugar provides 394 kcals per 100 grams; wholemeal bread provides 216; and potatoes, traditionally the slimmer's great no-no, provide a mere 80 kcals per 100 grams. However, if you fry potatoes to make what the British call chips and the Americans call fries, their energy content triples—to 250 kcals per 100 grams. Sweet soft-drinks commonly provide about 175 kcals per 100 ml (which is roughly 100 grams). You can drink a litre in a day without suppressing appetite: that's an additional 1750 kcals before you even start eating: adding more than 50 per cent to your required daily intake without you even noticing.

Fats too, like carbohydrates, are composed entirely of carbon, hydrogen, and oxygen. But again, these three simple elements can be combined in a virtual infinity of ways and fats too are immensely variable. Lard and suet are 'hard' fats. Chicken fat is softer. The fats of fish and many seeds are so soft that they manifest as oils at room temperatures. Waxes are fats which only a few animals can digest (such as the birds known as honey-eaters which induce other animals including humans to break into bees' nests so that they can then clean up the residue—but they prefer the wax to the honey.) Cholesterol is a peculiar form of fat. Chemically speaking, some fats are 'long-chain', meaning they have very big molecules; and some are short-chain, with smaller molecules. 'Saturated fats' contain as much hydrogen as it is chemically possible for them to contain, while 'unsaturated fats' contain less hydrogen than is theoretically possible. Broadly speaking, the fats of land animals (notably mammals) tend to be hard; and hard fats tend to be highly saturated. The oils of plants and fish tend (on the whole) to be highly unsaturated. Those that are particularly unsaturated are said to be 'polyunsaturated'.

With the possible exception of some waxes which humans find indigestible, all fats can be 'burnt' in the body as a potent source of energy. Indeed, weight for weight, fat provides twice as many calories—about 900 kcalories per 100 gram—as pure carbohydrate does. Thus a modest litre of cooking oil will provide about 8000 kcals—equivalent to three days'-worth of energy. In practice, fat tends to be diluted somewhat by water, so that butter and margarine provide about 740 kcals per 100 grams—still highly calorific. Animals including humans store surplus energy in the form of fat precisely because, weight for weight, it does provide so much energy. If human beings stored energy in the form of starch, like potatoes do, we would need to carry much more of it, and would be even more rotund. Westerners have high meat diets, which almost inevitably means that we have high fat diets. So it is that while traditional rural Chinese got only about 10 per cent of their calories from fat, westerners commonly get 40 per cent-plus from fat—largely animal fat. Ten per cent is perhaps too low, but 40 per cent is almost certainly too high. Very high fat diets evidently predispose not only to obesity, but also to various cancers (including breast cancer) and coronary heart disease. The ideal is probably between 20 and 30 per cent fat (although such 'ideals' are very hard to establish).

Fats, however, even more than carbohydrates, are a very important component of body structure. Every cell membrane is composed partly of protein and partly of 'lipid' (which is a fancy term for fat). Brains and nerves in general are particularly rich in structural fats. However, the fats needed to build cell membranes in general and brains and nerves in particular are of a special kind, loosely classed as 'essential fats'. Broadly speaking, these essential fats are of the polyunsaturated kind. Both the leaves and seeds of plants provide essential oils—and leaves and seeds provide different kinds, which are not interchangeable, so we need both leaves and seeds. Fish-oils tend to be especially rich in essential fats.

Saturated fats (and much of the unsaturated) on the whole are not 'essential'. They serve us merely as a source of energy. But in recent years nutritionists have emphasized our need for essential fats more and more. In particular, they have tended to recommend a high intake of fish, particularly of oily fish, such as mackerel. This is sound nutritional advice no doubt, but in reality, worldwide, fish is still only a minority food; yet already, as all the world knows, many if not most of the world's major fisheries are on their beam ends and some species that used to be taken for granted are now rare in some of their traditional grounds or even extinct. North Atlantic cod is a particularly shocking example. Fish farming can add prodigiously to the supply but raises huge problems of pollution (although these could be solved if we didn't try to do everything on the cheap).

In general, though, the advice to eat more and more fish really is 'unrealistic' for humanity at large. Besides, I once shared a conference platform with a nutritionist who warned the audience that their children were bound to grow up with defective brains unless they ate fish, fish, and more fish. But two of the principal speakers at the conference, who were both from inland village India and both exceedingly intelligent and eminently sane, pointed out that neither of them had eaten any fish at all until they came, as adults, to Europe. They had got all the essential fats they needed from plants.

Modern research shows, too, that the evil reputation that now attaches to beef—seen as a major source of harmful saturates—really applies mainly to beef raised on cereal, and fattened very quickly. Beef (and other animals) raised on natural pasture, generally more slowly and slaughtered when older, provide far more satisfactory proportions of unsaturated to saturated fats. More of this later.

Proteins are chemically more complicated than carbohydrates or fats. They too are composed primarily of carbon, hydrogen, and oxygen: but they also contain nitrogen and (generally) small amounts of sulphur. In reality, like polysaccharides, proteins are not so much molecules as 'macromolecules'. Polysaccharides are composed of long chains of sugars, and proteins are composed of (very) long chains of amino acids. In practice, most animal proteins contain various permutations drawn from a basic library of about 20 amino acids. About eight of these, such as lysine, methionine, and tryptophan, are said to be 'essential', while the rest are 'non-essential'. In practice, however, all of the amino acids are essential. It's just that the body cannot synthesize the ones that are called 'essential' for itself, so they have to be supplied ready-made in the food. But the body is able to make the so-called 'non-essential' amino acids for itself by converting the kinds it has enough of into the kind it feels it needs more of. In traditional nutritional parlance, proteins that contain all the essential amino acids roughly in the proportion that the human body requires were called 'first class'; and those that were (relatively) deficient in one or more of the essential amino acids were 'second class'. Broadly speaking, animal proteins tend to be first class, while plant proteins are often somewhat deficient (relatively) in one or other amino acid and so were considered to be second class.

Proteins are the main stuff (apart from water) of which flesh is made. The muscle—or at least the bit that does the contracting—is protein. Cell membranes in general are composed of protein plus fat. The haemoglobin in red blood cells is a protein. Antibodies are proteins. Some hormones are proteins. All enzymes are proteins— enzymes being the catalysts that enable the various chemical reactions to take place in the body; they are the drivers of metabolism. Clearly, if there can be degrees of essentialness, then proteins are among the most essential of all.

But there has been a revolution in thinking about proteins over the past few decades just as there has been in attitudes to dietary fibre, and to essential fats. For when I was at school in the late 1950s and early 1960s we were told as growing lads and budding biologists that human beings needed to eat protein in relatively vast quantities—'vast' in this context meaning that the total daily protein had to be equivalent to 12 to 15 per cent of the total intake of calories. Furthermore, we were told, this protein had to be 'first class'. It seemed, then, that we really had to consume a great deal of meat, fish, eggs, milk, and cheese—as much as possible. If we didn't, the message was, we would be feeble and (since antibodies are pure protein) we would be highly prone to infection.

There were many who doubted all this—including vegetarians, who may eat eggs and cheese (and possibly even fish, which is stretching things quite a lot) but in general consume very little animal protein. Some outstandingly able people were vegetarians, including George Bernard Shaw and Tolstoy (we will skate over Hitler). Indeed, some entire human populations were and are vegetarian to the point of vegan (no animal food at all), including many of the people of Southern India and rural Japan. Yet, demonstrably, vegans commonly live long and healthy lives and again, they include some of the world's most able people. Indeed, at the same time as we were being told that people needed vast amounts of meat if they were to survive at all, we were also being warned that people who for the most part ate little or no meat were breeding too fast.

Partly because of such general doubts, and partly because of some more critical experimental studies, it became clear by the 1970s that human protein needs had been greatly exaggerated. We don't need a diet that is 15 per cent protein. Healthy adults seem to get by perfectly well on five per cent or less. Neither do we need all the protein to be 'first class'. Few allegedly second-class proteins are *so* deficient in essential amino acids as to be positively useless. Besides, different 'second class' proteins tend to complement each other. So it is that cereal proteins tend to be low in lysine while pulse proteins (beans and so on) are high in lysine. So cereals and pulses together provide first class protein. In practice, the cereal-plus-pulse theme runs through all the great cuisines: rice and soy in China; rice or chapatti (wheat) and dhal in India; rice or cous-cous with beans (often broad beans) in the Middle East; tortilla (maize) with frijoles (kidney beans) in Mexico; and even beans-on-toast in Britain. People in traditional societies may not be versed in the niceties of biochemistry but they know what to do to stay alive. If they didn't they'd be dead.

The economic, social, and overall biological consequences of this shift in attitude to protein can hardly be overstated. In the days when we were supposed to need boundless protein, it seemed essential not simply to raise livestock, but to raise as much as possible. The intensive livestock systems including the battery cage for poultry, the factory farm for pigs, and the units for raising beef on 'surplus' cereal (so-called 'barley beef') that were just coming on line seemed to have arrived in the nick of time. Animal lovers who objected to such intensive farming on grounds of welfare and aesthetics were held to be irresponsible. Current mythology had it that we couldn't feed the human race without intensive husbandry. Contrariwise, cereals and pulses, including soya, were presented as 'stodge', to be grown primarily for animal feed.

Once the penny dropped—that actually, people don't need vast amounts of protein, and certainly don't need vast amounts of specifically animal protein—the whole picture reversed. Clearly, people could get all the protein they need from cereals and pulses alone: and while they were getting their protein, they would also get most of their energy, with a liberal dose of fibre too. Livestock that fed on cereals and pulses was *competing* with us, since we could perfectly well have eaten what they were eating. To be sure, meat and other animal products are highly desirable for a whole host of reasons. They provide essential minerals such as calcium and zinc that are not easily obtainable from plants in sufficient amounts, and vitamins such as B_{12} and some essential fats, and are certainly significant as sources of calories—especially in latitudes and in seasons where plants are not readily available. So don't write them off. But don't build the whole diet around them either.

So the shift in nutritional theory—towards much less protein, and particularly less animal protein—could and should have transformed the face of agriculture. It should have halted the frantic emphasis on livestock. But of course it did not. For reasons discussed in chapter 4, livestock can be highly lucrative: and where lucre leads these days, all human endeavour, including agriculture, is bound to follow. Of course the food industry claims that the livestock industry continues to flourish (although not everywhere) only because it meets 'consumer demand'—but this, as we will see, is far less true than industry likes to pretend, and indeed in large part is a simple lie (for money justifies untruth as well).

So, even though the shift in theory meant we no longer needed to emphasize livestock, the cash-wagon has rolled on. Currently we feed 50 per cent of the world's wheat and barley to livestock; 80 per cent of the maize; and well over 90 per cent of the soya. By 2050, on present trends, when the human population numbers nine billion, our livestock will be consuming enough good grain and pulses to feed another four billion—roughly equivalent to the total human population in the early 1970s when the United Nations held its first World Food Conference in Rome to discuss what it saw as a global food crisis. Just for good measure, too, various major crops, including maize, are now being turned into biofuel. To put the matter crudely, the race is on between poor children in poor countries, and SUVs. Since the fight in the modern world is bound to go to the rich, it's no contest.

There is a broader lesson in all this, too. If nutritional science had shown that human beings do need more and more meat, then this would have been seized upon as justification for a bigger and bigger (and more and more lucrative) livestock industry. Since modern science shows the precise opposite, the relevant science is simply ignored. Thus we see the role of science in modern politics and commerce in general. Science at its best and in its unadulterated form aspires to discover objective, factual truth. It would be safer, you might think, to base political strategies on objective factual truth where this is possible. But when the factual truth is inconvenient to the powers-that-be, they simply ignore it, or find some tame scientist who will say whatever he or she is paid to say. But I will come to that.

The last broad category of essential foods is or are loosely classed as 'micronutrients': essential to be sure, but required only in minute quantities—typically in milligrams or even micrograms per day, or at most only a few grams. Micronutrients may be considered under three headings: minerals, vitamins, and a newly identified and little understood collection of what for convenience I will call 'paravitamins'. *

---

* *Three novel nutritional terms have become fashionable in recent years: 'functional foods'; 'nutraceuticals'; and 'phytonutrients'. Functional foods are food of any kind that seem to have some beneficial effect over and above their nutritional content. That is, they seem in some way to function as tonics or medicines, and not simply as sources of energy or raw material. The term 'nutraceutical' is commonly used synonymously with 'functional food'. 'Phytonutrient' strictly speaking should mean anything nutritious found in plants, but in practice (since most nutraceuticals are plant-based, and since bacteria and fungi are commonly classed as 'plants' although they very obviously are not), the term 'phytonutrient' is also used synonymously with 'nutraceutical'. All these terms are vague, however, and used in various contexts. I am coining the term 'paravitamin' to describe the active ingredients that the various 'functional foods' (alias nutraceuticals alias phytonutrients) apparently contain. I would not bore you with this except that all these novel terms are heard so often these days, not least because functional foods are now such big business. Again, we find that there is some excellent science behind the general idea: but once ideas become commercialized, as all ideas seem bound to do these days, they also become subject to spin, and confusion is bound to reign.*

Minerals are chemical elements: non-metals such as iodine which is a component of the thyroid hormone thyroxine; and metals such as sodium and potassium which are essential to maintain the integrity of cell membranes; iron which is a key component of haemoglobin; calcium which has all kinds of functions (in addition to its role in the structure of bones and teeth); and so on and so on. One way or another the body makes use of and therefore has need of about a third of all the elements in the periodic table. Some of those elements (probably most) are vital in small amounts but toxic in larger amounts. Copper is an obvious example. Sodium too is essential—but if taken in very great amounts over a long period it predisposes to high blood pressure, aka hypertension, which in turn predisposes to stroke and increases the risk of coronary heart disease. It is rare to consume too much copper but excess sodium intake has become usual in the western world because we eat so much salt—sodium chloride; not so much as a condiment, but as a major ingredient of processed foods, freely deployed both as a preservative and to enhance the flavour, including sweet foods such as ketchup and some breakfast cereals.

Our need for vitamins began to become apparent at least by the 17th century, when sailors and doctors realized that scurvy was caused by nutritional deficiency—and could be countered by eating citrus fruit such as limes. By the 19th century it was clear that the essential ingredient was vitamin C—alias ascorbic acid. Ascorbic acid, it is now known, is one of the body's many 'anti-oxidants'. We rely on oxygen for respiration but it is chemically lively stuff and if it escapes in various chemical forms into the body at large it can oxidize the body tissues themselves, with huge damage. Several vitamins (and many other bodily ingredients, such as uric acid) are now known to function as anti-oxidants—and we would be sunk without them (although recently there have been warnings from on high that we should not eat too much of them. But then the general advice I got from my granny—don't eat too much of anything; or, 'a little bit of what you fancy does you good', seems to cover the case).

Throughout the 19th but especially in the 20th centuries more and more such vitamins were identified, all very different chemically, all essential, all leading to disorder that could be fatal if deficient. Mostly they are known by letters, such as vitamin A—deficiency of which leads among other things to dryness of the eyeball ('xeroph-thalmia') and hence to blindness. Relative deficiency of folic acid in early pregnancy (which effectively means pre-pregnancy) apparently increases the chances of spina bifida in the developing foetus. And so on.

'Paravitamins' I am defining as the active ingredients in 'functional foods' or 'nutraceuticals', as described in the footnote. If paravitamins are lacking, this does not necessarily lead to overt disease—which is why it took so long to identify these agents. But if they are present then in various ways they seem to be health-promoting. One of the best known is or are various plant sterols which, when present, apparently lower blood cholesterol and so, in theory at least, should reduce the likelihood of coronary heart disease.

Some hard-nosed sceptics doubt the validity of paravitamins. They find it implausible that the body should require such odd and unrelated things generally components of plants. Besides, because deficiency of paravitamins does not generally lead to obvious disease or death (in the short term), it is very hard to measure their effects; and many scientists, of a certain type, dismiss phenomena that are not easily measurable and so seem unreliable.

But as the great 20th century Ukrainian-American biologist Theodosius Dobzhansky commented in an essay in 1973, 'Nothing in biology makes sense except in light of evolution'; and if you look at paravitamins in an evolutionary light, they make perfect sense. So it is that our ancestors—our first human ancestors, and before that our australopithecine and then our apish ancestors—included a great variety of plants in their diet. Modern hunter-gathering people commonly consume a hundred or more different species. Until the past few thousand years, all the plants that people ate were wild—and wild plants include a great many potent biochemical agents, many of which the plant produces in order to ward off insects and other parasites, and for many other purposes as well. Thus, our hunter-gathering and pre-human ancestors were exposed, every day, to a huge variety of different chemicals produced by plants for all kinds of purposes, many of which were toxins. In addition, in nature, we are exposed to a great many bacteria and fungi, ever present on food in one way and another: and, biochemically speaking, bacteria and fungi are just as accomplished as plants are.

Animals cope with weird substances in many different ways. If they consume what is all too obviously poisonous, they die (although most, like rats, have clever ways of sampling and rejecting novel foods before they consume too much). Many herbivores avoid trouble by eating only small amounts of any one plant: goats and ostriches do this. Others develop specific enzymes and extensions of the gut to help them overcome specific toxins that they encounter in large amounts—and so the koala has a caecum (a blind extension of the gut) which is packed with bacteria and protozoa, which break down the many fierce toxins, resins, and fibre in the leaves of its favoured eucalyptus.

But evolution, most generally, leads to adaptation. An animal may first evolve the means to cope with some plant toxin, for example by developing some detoxifying enzyme. At first, the body merely excretes the break-down products produced by the detoxification. But as the generations pass the body finds ways of utilizing the breakdown products of the original toxin—and these may then may function for example as anti-oxidants (and it is hard to have too many). So we can imagine that a body comes eventually to depend upon weird agents that are present in nature—mostly in plants, but also produced by other creatures such as bacteria and fungi—and might originally have been toxic. This, after all, is precisely how early bacteria came to terms with oxygen itself—first poisoned by it, and then becoming reliant upon it.

I suggest, then, that our need for a variety—perhaps or even probably a huge variety—of weird substances that are present in nature but are hard to identify or pin down, is entirely plausible. Indeed I have developed the concept of 'pharmacological impoverishment': the condition that animals or any of us are in when our diet is deficient in these agents (see 'Functional Food and Pharmacological Impoverishment', in *Future Food*, Caroline Walker Trust, London, 1999). The term 'nutraceuticals' is not entirely inappropriate since these recondite agents have some characteristics of food and also some characteristics of drugs, or at least of tonics. (But I prefer the term 'paravitamin' for reasons described in the footnote).

I also suggest that on modern diets, we are extremely likely to be pharmacologically impoverished. We consume nothing like the range of plants that our ancestors ate—and that we are presumably adapted to; and most of the plants we do consume are domesticated, bred over many generations primarily for yield and appearance, so that much of the biochemical variety and subtlety has been bred out of them.

What I do find objectionable, strange, and deeply pernicious is the modern approach to paravitamins. The obvious lesson is that we should eat, as our ancestors ate, a huge variety of plants—and especially wild plants; and fungi, too, and fermented foods. We need to acknowledge that it is logically impossible to identify all the paravitamins our bodies might need: only by eating many different things can we be reasonably sure of covering all bases. So the nutritionists should be saying: 'Variety, variety, variety'. Some of them are saying this. But many, including many who are paid the most and have the biggest laboratories to work in, are seeking instead to identify particular paravitamins, and where possible to synthesize them in the laboratory, and then adding them to processed foods. They do this not because it is nutritionally sensible and good for human beings, but because it is profitable. If people were simply encouraged to grow herbs, and sometimes where feasible to gather them, there would be no profit for food processors. So instead we must be told that the only way to obtain ingredients that are essential to us is by buying particular foods produced by particular companies with particular bands of shareholders to answer to, at huge cost. This is the way of the modern world: not to do things that are merely sensible and beneficial; but to do those things—and only those things—that bring profit to big companies and at the same time increase the power of the political parties who are financed by those companies. Game set and match. Yet, biologically speaking—which is what really matters—those huge dominating companies are redundant. This is the nonsense we have to escape from.

One last point, of huge practical importance. There is more and more literature on 'self-dosing' in animals. That is, wild animals that are feeling a bit poorly or have some physiological need (such as pregnancy) actively seek out particular minerals or herbs or tree leaves which they seem to *know* will do them good. The elephants and antelopes of the savannah will go to enormous lengths to find salt to lick. Macaws in Brazil eat kaolin, natural clay with great absorptive qualities, which evidently helps them to sequester the various toxins they pick up in their food. Every cat-lover has seen their pets gobbling grass from time to time (which tends to make them sick—which of course can be very therapeutic; just what the vet ordered). It's becoming common practice in zoos to give all animals access to wild vegetation, and to plant specific herbs—and there is anecdotal evidence at least that they eat the herbs when their stomachs are upset. I have watched sheep, alleged grass-lovers, making long migrations across fields to nibble the last bit of tree— seeking the variety, and whatever special stuff is in the leaves. I have a farmer friend who allows his dairy cattle access to as much wild herbage as possible—and found that they have a particular predilection for Japanese knot-grass, which at present is running riot over Britain and ruining many an ecosystem. Most dairy farmers spend thousands of pounds a year on vet fees but his vet bill in 2008, for more than 100 cows, was £13.00—and that was for a cow that had fallen foul of some barbed wire. All this is peripheral and ad hoc evidence, but to my mind is strong evidence, that paravitamins are real, and they matter. This should influence both our diet and the way we keep our livestock. Organic farmers and health-food aficionados are often mocked from on high for insisting that 'natural' diets are the best. But, of course, in principle, they are absolutely right. There is more to life than second-form chemistry.

It is possible, of course, to write forever about the intricacies of nutrition: biological, historical, political. But the above, I suggest, includes everything that everyone really ought to know. Of course it is complicated—at least in detail. The powers-that-be revel in the complexity. The more complicated it appears the more it is inaccessible—and the more we are apparently dependent on experts;

on the powers that be, who alone are able to handle the knowledge. Obfuscation and esotericism has been the con trick of charlatans through the ages.

Far more striking, however, and far more important, is the underlying simplicity of modern nutritional theory. For when you boil it down, what does it amount to? It can be summarized in nine words:

'Plenty of plants, not much meat, and maximum variety'.

That's it. All the thousands of textbooks and diet books and healthy eating books that occupy miles and miles and miles of shelf-space in hundreds and hundreds of libraries and bookshops can be expressed in this one brief adage: '*Plenty of plants, not much meat, and maximum variety*'. That's *it*.

So to the second question: What is possible? Can we produce the food we need—and if so, how?

Can we produce enough? If so—how?

If you tell the story one way, then the task of feeding nearly seven billion people now and nine billion by 2050 looks very difficult indeed—as outlined in chapter 1. A billion people still go short yet most of the world's most fertile land is already cultivated and much of that is eroded or otherwise degraded, and the oil that fires present-day industrial agriculture is running out—and so too, much more importantly, is the water. It all starts to look impossible. The powers that be—the consortium of governments, corporates, and banks—have played on this in recent years. In the early days of industrialization after World War II they told us that surpluses were the problem—but now they queue up to tell us that we face disaster unless we double output in the next 40 years, and that this requires us to industrialize even more than we have been doing, with even more high tech.

It seems reasonable to assume that elected governments should be on our side—yet it can be hard to believe that present-day governments really are taking the world's food problems seriously; and although they claim to base their policies on science, it is hard to believe that many of those scientists know anything about farming. For we are told in the British government's latest 'Foresight' report on *The Future of Food and Farming* (January 24 2011) that the world as a whole has about 4.6 billion hectares of land that can reasonably be called agricultural. So the question becomes, 'Is it possible to feed nine billion people, well and sustainably, on 4.6 billion hectares?'

A traditional farmer would answer, 'Easily!'. For 4.6 billion hectares shared between nine billion people works out at half a hectare each—just over an acre. That should be plenty. In Britain, for example, the average wheat yield is now around eight tonnes per hectare. One kilogram of wheat provides around 3000 kcals of food energy, at more than ten per cent protein—which is more than enough energy and protein to feed an adult for a day. Since there are 365 days in a year, each person requires just over a third of a tonne of wheat per annum (or the equivalent thereof)—so one hectare, producing eight tonnes, could provide the macronutrients, the basis of a staple diet, for more than 20 people. That's ten times as much as the average that's needed.

Of course, the cosseted, supplemented wheatfields of Britain are far more productive than much of the world. Cattle and sheep, grazing and browsing in semi-desert, hardly produce a hundredth of this. But many systems worldwide are far more productive than Britain's arable—including the traditional small mixed units of South-East Asia, where rice and horticulture are tightly integrated with fish, ducks, and pigs, and everything grows all year round. Even the arable farmers of the Sahel, who hope to produce about one tonne of sorghum per hectare, are producing enough. Overall, then, we ought to be able to say—"No panic!" The prime task, surely, is simply to encourage good farmers to farm, usually in the way that they do traditionally, and to make it possible for them to do so. The secondary task is to find ways to enable farmers worldwide to do what they do with minimum collateral damage—but then if you look closely at traditional systems you find that many are wonderfully conservative and wildlife-friendly (as in the traditional mixed farms of South-East Asia); far more so than western high-tech systems.

In truth, traditional farms, at their best (when they are given a chance to work properly!) are just what the world needs, at least in principle. If we are truly to provide good food for everybody forever we clearly need farms that are productive, sustainable, and resilient (able to change direction as conditions change)—and to achieve this we may simply take Nature itself as our model; for Nature has been wonderfully productive for the pasts 3.8 billion years, without interruption, although conditions have changed absolutely in all that time, several times over, from pole-to-pole ice to pole-to-pole tropics, or very nearly. Nature achieves all this by being both diverse and integrated: many thousands of species in any one place, interacting synergistically. It is sustainable because—perforce—it is wonderfully economical. It uses no resources that cannot be replaced and provides a master-class in re-cycling. Waste for one creature is provender for another.

The farming equivalent of nature's diversity is polyculture—mixed farming; while minimum input with constant recycling in essence is organic farming. Organic farming need not be the absolute requirement, relentlessly pursued. But it should be the default position: what farmers do unless there is a very good biological reason to do something else. Thus, common sense and basic biology tell us that to feed ourselves well and reliably we need mixed, integrated farms in which organic farming is the norm.

Such farms are bound to be complex—and so they must be labour intensive. When units are complex and labour-intensive there is little or no advantage is scale-up. So in general enlightened farms should be small. Small, mixed farms are best suited to local delivery (though of course we need trade as well—*fair* trade). In other words, the *structure* of the kinds of farms the world really needs should be traditional. In Britain such farming reached its height in the late 1950s. Overall, despite the best efforts of big industry and big governments to sweep it is aside, it is still the norm. We should be very grateful for this. For although the powers-that-be assure us that the world is in desperate need of high-tech industrialization (which is the most conspicuous message from *The Future of Food and Farming*) it seems that traditional farms, generally small, mixed, labour-intensive and at least quasi-organic, still provide about 70 per cent of the world's food. If the world's governments and their attendant experts were truly on the side of humanity, and of our fellow creatures and the fabric of the Earth, they would be putting good science and the weight of law and our taxpayers' money behind farms that are small to medium-sized, labour-intensive, mixed, highly integrated, and mostly organic.

So why don't they?

Why don't we farm as if we intended to feed people?

It is perfectly reasonable to regard the powers-that-be with scepticism, and indeed with cynicism. Truly, their attitude towards agriculture this past four decades (in particular) has been a disgrace. We can reasonably suggest, indeed, that the powers-that-be want agriculture to be as industrialized as possible, and as high tech as possible, because 'they', the powers that be, are doing so well out of it. Firstly, industrialized systems by their nature are centralized: a few big companies dominate. They are much easier to deal with than battalions of small and often stroppy farmers. Industrialization leaves governments very much in control.

Secondly, the farm industry, like every other kind of industry in this age of finance capitalism, is designed above all to make money. Governments can count this money very easily—it's mostly in the hands of a few big companies—and then they can call it GDP: Gross Domestic Product. Increase in GDP year by year is called 'economic growth' and—which for governments like Britain's is the principal, if not the sole, index of success, although it has nothing whatever to do with general well-being. So in farming, industrialization *per se* gives the illusion of economic growth even though no one actually benefits (except bankers and shareholders).

Indeed industrialized agriculture as it now stands is expressly designed, not to produce good food for everyone, but to produce the most money in the shortest time. This may sound cynical to the

point of ludicrousness but the reality of this is behind every state-
ment that anyone in high places ever seems to make, even if it is
not what they intend. Thus in Britain, successive Secretaries of State
for Agriculture, including Caroline Spelman who is in currently in
charge (February 2011) have emphasized the need for Britain to
produce more of its own food to increase food security—and this
seems fine and commonsensical. The previous Secretary of State,
from a different political party, Hilary Benn, said much the same.
Both, however, in their speeches, are careful to add that Britain's
farmers must 'compete' on the world market. In other words, our
farmers should produce more food—but only if they can do it more
cheaply than the Brazilians. Otherwise, Britain should simply buy
what it needs from the Brazilians.

To be sure, this is an improvement on the British government's
attitude to farming over the past 30 years (the rot really started
with Thatcher at the end of the 1970s). Thus in 2002 I shared a
speaking platform in Oxford with a senior civil servant, who had
been knighted for his sterling contributions to agriculture, who told
us that Britain's farming should go the way of its coal-mining—
which Thatcher put a stop to in the late 1980s. After all, said this
distinguished knight, we can generally buy food more cheaply from
abroad than we can grow it—and if the Brazilians charge too much
we can always go to East Timor, or whoever is most desperate at
the time. No further discussion needed. In the same way, we could
buy coal more cheaply from Poland or China—so go for it. He was,
he told us, reflecting Treasury opinion; and in this age of finance
capitalism, the Treasury rules. Actually I reckon that Britain's farming would have gone the way of its mining if the government had
thought they could get away with it. But a countryside without
farming would be expensive too; and besides, too many people in
high places, including government, had and have at least some vested interest in farming, if only as landowners, so such a policy would
have been hard to push through. But it wasn't for lack of intent.

So farming in Britain has survived, albeit by a whisker, and in
a form that is often most regrettable; and, now, even governments
are beginning to recognize that global warming is a reality, so we

cannot assume that Brazil will continue as a cornucopia; and even if it does, the Chinese will soon be able to outbid everybody else on the world market; and so on and so on. So on the face of things they seem to be supporting agriculture once more.

But governments like Britain's still don't get the point: that agriculture that feeds people, and can go on doing so, must be rooted in sound biology. They talk constantly about the need for 'efficiency', the watchword of the neoliberal economy—but by this they mean 'cash efficiency': the monetary cost of production *versus* the cash value of the output. But the monetary values are entirely arbitrary and whimsical—dependent for example on the price of oil which is *not*, as the market zealots claim, related directly to the physical scarcity of oil, but is entirely a matter of bargaining power and who is at war with whom. That the fate of all humanity and indeed of all life on Earth should rest on such politicking is absurd. It is indeed necessary to maximize efficiency. But this should mean *biological* efficiency.

Biological efficiency

'Maximising biological efficiency' means producing as much good food as possible per acre or per hectare, by means that are minimally destructive. We can reasonably focus on the macronutrients—energy and protein; and if we also strive for maximum variety we will take care of the essential fats and of the micronutrients in passing. So how do we do this?

Well, in the 1950s, when the zeal for protein was at its height, nutritionists told us that the central task was to maximise livestock: meat, eggs, and dairy. But we can get all the protein we want, as well as the bulk of our energy, from plants: more particularly from the crops that are generally called 'staples'—cereals, pulses, tubers, and also various oilseed crops which can be major sources of calories. Grow these in sufficient and the problem of feeding people is all over bar the shouting. Feeding people, looked at in these simplest of terms, really is easy.

The most important staples are the cereals—the big, nutritious seeds of certain grasses: wheat, rice, and maize (which the Americans call corn), barley, rye, oats, sorghum, millet, and teff, the local grain of Ethiopia. The pulses are the beans—soya, the various kidney beans, and broad beans; peanuts (alias groundnuts); chickpeas; pigeon peas; lentils; and peas. Some other non-grass seeds also serve as grains: quinoa and amaranth from South America; 'wild rice' from North America. Oilseed crops include rapeseed (known in the New World as canola), which is grown the world over; sunflowers (which prefer warm climes); olives (primarily in the Mediterranean); and more and more palm oil (in the tropics). Peanuts, maize and soya are also significant oilseed crops. Nuts can be very important—notably the coconut in southern India and southeast Asia. The world's most important tubers are the potato, plus cassava, yams, taro, and sweet potatoes.

By far the most important worldwide are wheat, rice, and maize. Between them, directly or indirectly (after conversion to meat by livestock) they provide humanity with a half of all our calories, and two thirds of our protein. But the other staples are important too. Barley is used largely for animal feed and brewing these days but is an admirable food crop in its own right with particular value where the land is salty and on high mountains (it replaced wheat in ancient Mesopotamia as the Euphrates silted up and the land was salinated and nowadays is much favoured in Tibet and Nepal). Rye and oats withstand extremes of climate. Sorghum and especially millet are crops of extreme dryland—and peanuts alias ground nuts are even more so. Coconuts are wonderful by the sea, drenched in brine and sometimes seeming to grow out of pure sand, tethered by their astonishingly tough and prolific roots. Potatoes used to be written off as the great no-no. Now it is clear that they can be an adequate source even of protein, at least for adults, and for many people they are the greatest single source of vitamin C.

In short, all we really need to do to ensure that the world is at least adequately fed—that people can at least get by—is to grow staple crops in the places where they grow best. They are the priority. Staple crops in general are grown on the 'field scale': the ground is ploughed and the seeds (or sometimes small tubers) are planted en masse, thousands or millions at a time. Then they are harvested en masse, typically these days by machines (notably combine harvesters). Such field-scale agriculture is called 'arable', from the Latin word for 'ear', as in ear of corn.

However, although staples are undoubtedly the priority, and although we would at least stay alive if we had enough of them, they do not by themselves provide a complete diet. An all-staple diet would in general leave us short of some essential fats; some minerals (such as zinc); some vitamins; many paravitamins; and a further boost to the quality of the protein would probably be no bad thing despite my earlier comments—just to be on the safe side. An all-staple diet would also be rather tedious, although many people in the history of the world have lived almost exclusively on one staple or another: many Asians on rice; the poor Irish and western Scots of the early 19th century on potatoes; many Scots almost entirely on oats; and so on. So we need two more classes of agriculture to run alongside or amongst the arable. These are horticulture; and pastoral.

Horticulture is the art, science, and craft of growing fruit and vegetables, herbs and spices. Horticulture may be practiced on a very large scale and sowing and harvesting (or picking) may be highly mechanized but nonetheless, in principle at least, the plants are tended individually; the word 'horticulture' derives from the Latin *hortus* meaning garden, and is indeed appropriate. Horticulturalists who specialize in food crops are often called 'market gardeners'. Fruit specialists are commonly called 'growers'. Horticultural crops are valuable for their essential fats (especially the kinds that occur in leaves); for their micronutrients; their fibre content; occasionally for their energy and protein—as in avocadoes; and for their flavour. However, as a few pioneer farmers are now showing worldwide, it is also possible and can be well worthwhile to grow some staples on the horticultural scale as well—not just pulses, which gardeners already grow, but also small-scale cereals; especially of rare varieties that are no longer grown commercially but often have special qualities (such as wheat with less gluten, or with gluten of a kind that is less liable to cause gluten intolerance).

Horticultural crops and staples between them can provide a diet that is excellent both nutritionally and gastronomically as many a healthy and cheerful vegan bears witness to—including many a traditional Asian, in India, China, and rural Japan. Spices, herbs, and various fermentations as in the Chinese and Japanese soy and the Japanese miso certainly help both in flavour and with paravitamins.

Pastoral farming, from the Latin *pastor* meaning care, is the art, science, and craft of raising livestock—though in truth in many modern intensive units the benighted beasts receive very little care.

At first sight, you may conclude that pastoral farming is a waste of time, effort, and space: that livestock are simply a drain on the world's resources. Many a vegetarian has argued thus. After all, human beings can live very well indeed on an all-plant diet. Indeed in many respects vegans are particularly healthy—largely or almost entirely avoiding the modern major killers of coronary heart disease, and various cancers and diabetes. Furthermore, if the aim is to produce maximum protein and calories per hectare, then plants seem a far better bet. Yields of crops vary enormously from region to region: a tonne of grain per hectare of sorghum in some dry African field may be perfectly respectable, while a highly-mechanised arable farmer in Britain's East Anglia would be disappointed with less than twelve tonnes of wheat per hectare. But in either case, the yield of protein and calories per hectare is generally between five and ten times greater than it would be if the same field were used for cattle. Cattle need to eat about 10 grams of plant protein for every one gram of meat or meat protein that they produce (and they drink staggering quantities of water as well).

Despite all this—that livestock don't seem to be nutritionally vital and seem tremendously inefficient—pastoral farming is very important indeed. The oft-bruited generalization—that we could most easily feed the world if everyone was vegetarian—is simply not true. To be sure, it would be easier to feed a world full of vegans than a world of hamburger and fried chicken addicts. In absolute terms, it would be eminently possible to feed the former, and it is already obvious that we cannot cope with the latter. Nonetheless: there is no system of all-plant agriculture that could not be made more efficient, in biological terms, by adding in a few livestock, provided they are of the right kind, and are kept in the right numbers, in the right ways. The trouble begins, as always, only when farmers (or the corporates and governments who make farming policy) stop thinking in terms of biological efficiency and long-term possibility, and think only of cash.

For instance: In many parts of the world, at least in some seasons, it is very difficult to raise crops at all. Arable is all but impossible when the land is too high, steep, cold, or wet or if it rains too much in the season when the grain should be ripening. Horticulture is possible almost everywhere if you invest enough in it but may languish for lack of water. But animals of one kind or another muddle through anywhere—living as camels and goats may do on the most meagre of leaves that poke between the thorns of desert trees, or as reindeer do on lichen, or as long-wooled sheep and shaggy cattle do in British hills on the coarse grasses that grow between the heather; and in times of drought or the depths of winter there may be nothing to eat at all except for beasts that fattened in better times. In all countries, too, the manure of livestock has been a prime source of soil fertility—and still should be. The dust-bowl of the American prairies in the 1930s would surely have been less dramatic (so many agriculturalists surmised) if the soil had been enriched with manure, and had not been surrendered so absolutely to grain. In many tropical countries the dung of cattle serves both as fuel and as the 'daub' with which to build houses of a kind that can endure for many decades (and centuries if the walls are plastered). For good measure, for people worldwide, cattle are significant transport—as of course are camels and horses; and in many countries horses are also a source of milk (fermented in central Asia to make *kvass*) and of meat (as in France, Belgium, and Switzerland. Horse meat is very good). All in all, then, we must take livestock seriously—even though, in the modern industrial systems, geared to the maximization of cash, they are subject to such cruelties and produced so profligately.

For animals that can digest cellulose (with microbial help) it is their most important source of energy, usually by far. A cornucopia is thus opened up to them, for cellulose is the most abundant by far of all the organic macromolecules in nature: there must be trillions of tons of it out there. We, straight-gutted humans, cannot digest cellulose. But we do eat the animals that can. So via cattle, sheep, and all the other specialist herbivores, we too can partake of nature's most generous feast.

Looked at ecologically and agronomically, livestock can usefully be divided into two main categories: the specialist herbivores, and the omnivores. The specialist herbivores are able to digest cellulose—the stuff of which plant cell walls are made. At least, they do not digest it with their own gut enzymes, but they maintain vast armies of bacteria and protozoa in their guts which digest it for them, and the animal then absorbs the organic acids that result. The animal then converts these acids into sugars. Ruminants, which in this context means cattle, sheep, goats, and deer; and pseudo-ruminants, which are the camels, llamas, guanacos, alpacas, and vicunas, harbour their helpful microbes in the fore-gut—in a vast stomach known as the rumen. The 'hind-gut digesters'—horses, elephants, rabbits, guinea-pigs—keep their symbiont flora and fauna in a diversion of the hind-gut, known as a caecum. Of all these herbivores, worldwide, cattle and sheep are by far the most important, but all the rest are locally important too—guinea pigs in Peru and rabbits not least in China (and Malta).

Pigs and poultry, by contrast, are omnivores. Potentially, they eat anything. Indeed they eat the same kinds of things as we do, except that they have lower aesthetic standards (and both pigs and poultry to some extent seem to be able to derive at least some energy from cellulose, and may supplement their diets with grass**).

** *Wild pigs have long hind guts and can derive significant amounts of energy from cellulose. Modern pigs have been bred with short hind guts and need rich food—mostly cereal—just as people do. We should reverse the trend of modern pig-breeding, and develop new strains of grass-feeders. The Berkshire is among the existing types that do well on a diet high in grass. But the Berkshire is not considered 'economic' and in recent years has become a rare breed.*

In recent years, the vegans have found support from an unlikely quarter—the modern livestock industry. For in these days of cheap oil and general corporate carve-up, it can be cheaper to produce beef and milk from grain than from grass (given that the real costs of grain-feeding are largely unquantified). The modern commercial lobby likes to point out that grass-fed cattle (and other ruminants) produce more methane per animal than grain-fed cattle. Methane is a potent greenhouse gas and so, says the commercial lobby, feeding grain is good, and feeding cattle on grass is bad. Politicians, who on the whole know nothing about agriculture and don't want to be bothered with it, but are anxious to maximize wealth, of course believe the commercial lobby. In fact, we are told, grain-feeding comes with a bonus: it is profitable, and it also allows agri-business people to claim that they are caring for the environment.

It was left to an agricultural journalist, Graham Harvey, to point out in his excellent *The Carbon Fields* (Grass Roots, Somerset, 2008), that this is serious nonsense. To be sure, *individual* animals produce more methane when fed on grass than they do when fed on grain. But if the grazing is properly managed, then grassland as a whole *is a net absorber of carbon*—it is in fact a carbon sink. For grass grows best when its roots are invaded by symbiotic fungi: the root and fungus together form a mycorrhiza. The fungi greatly increase the efficiency of the roots and indeed, some wild plants won't grow at all without their mycorrhizae. Pine trees, so widespread throughout the world, depend very heavily on their mycorrhizae. Orchid seeds generally won't germinate without their fungal assistants.

When grass is suddenly, and heavily grazed, the leaves of the grass are nipped back practically to soil level, and a large proportion of the roots—which can be many metres deep—die off, because the leaves can no longer support them. These roots together with their mycorrizae, are rich in carbon: carbon is, in fact, the main stuff of which they are made. You might suppose that once the roots die, the organic carbon would simply decay and find its way back into the atmosphere in the form of carbon dioxide. But the carbon that has been trapped by the mycorrhizal fungi is in a peculiar organic form that does not decay easily. It just stays in the soil. Hence the grassland, when intensively grazed, finishes up sequestering more carbon than is released—even though the cattle are producing methane.

So the trick is to allow cattle to graze very intensively—to over-graze, in fact, most farmers would say—but then to move them on (commonly, these days with the aid of electric fences) and allow the grass a long time to recover. A great deal of research on farms, and in the wild, now shows that with such a system, the organic content of the soil—meaning the carbon content—increases very rapidly. In short, whatever way you look at it, grazing is a good thing: and well-managed cattle on grassland could bring enormous net benefit both to human nutrition and to the whole world environment. Contrary to the commercial propaganda, well managed grazing would help to *alleviate* global warming.

One anecdotal point. Twenty or so million years ago, the whole world was beginning to cool down (for reasons we needn't go into here). As the world cools it becomes drier (less evaporation and more water locked in ice). So trees give way to grass. So the past 20 million years or so—through the geological periods known as the Miocene, Pliocene, Pleistocene, and Holocene (the present)—have been the great age of grassland. Throughout the Miocene and into the Pleistocene the world teemed with grazing animals of all kinds, with the ruminants becoming more and more prominent. We still see the general kind of pattern on Africa's grassland, which has horses (zebras), rhinos, and elephants—but overwhelmingly has ruminants in the form of cattle (buffalo) and antelopes (wildebeest and the rest). All these grazing ruminants would have produced astonishing amounts of methane. Yet, throughout the Miocene and onwards, the world carried on getting cooler until we finished up with the succession of Ice Ages in the Pleistocene. Wild ruminants graze in exactly the same way as is recommended for domestic cattle: over-grazing in one spot, and then moving on, and allowing plenty of time for recovery. Again we see that nature knows best, and the best policy is to follow its lead. One final note: the grass fed to domestic cattle should be wild pasture. Modern commercial rye-grass is enormously highly fertilized and does not form such good mycorrhizae, and is most unlikely to provide a net carbon sink.

Guided by such principles—principles rooted in elementary biology—the structure of the farm defines itself, too. Of course, no two farms are exactly alike. Traditionally, some of those up in the hills of Britain were devoted almost entirely to sheep; others in the pampas of Argentina were almost all cattle; and so on. Yet, traditionally, *most* farms worldwide had a similar overall structure. All marched to the drum of their local ecology and although landscapes and climates vary enormously over the globe the fundamental principles of ecology are the same, just as the laws of physics are the same.

Traditionally, farms were generally 'mixed'. There would be some arable—with several different species of grain, pulse, and other staples; and, often, several or many varieties of each. There would be some horticulture: at the very least, traditional farms all had cottage gardens. Both the main classes of livestock—the specialist herbivores and the omnivores—would be fitted in as required, with the cattle and sheep feeding both on permanent pasture that could not be ploughed for cereal, in wet meadows and/or in the hills, and spending a season or so in the arable fields between crops. Two such farms I have seen at first hand come to mind. One was in China, in the mid 1990s. The entire landscape was basically devoted to rice, the flooded paddies stretching from hill to hill. But of course there was higher ground; and on the higher ground the people grew every kind of vegetable (with yams conspicuous). Between the young rice stalks squeezed flotillas of ducks, feeding on the algae and the myriad invertebrates that bred in the paddy water. I didn't see fish, but rice farmers typically, and traditionally, raise grass carp—a virtually vegetarian species that likes tropical waters. In the village there were pigs and chickens in the road, feeding on whatever they could find. Perfect. By contrast—and yet essentially similar—I recall one of the first English farms I ever saw, in the 1950s. Dairy cattle were raised on temporary leys between the arable crops largely for butter, and also on permanent hill pasture; and—very modern for its day!—young pigs who were fed on surplus corn were given a boost in growth with the whey left over from butter-making. All very neat, and biologically impeccable.

Two final refinements. These days—and this is one of the few bright lights on an otherwise dismal horizon—there has been increasing interest in *agroforestry*: raising crops and livestock of all kinds in various degrees of integration with trees; treating the trees as very much part of the farm ecosystem. The best example I know of this in Britain is in Suffolk, where Martin Wolfe (a scientist turned farmer) raises grain, potatoes, and practices horticulture, between rows of trees of various classes—hazel and willow grown for short-term timber; fruit trees, scattered to reduce the spread of infection but close enough for pollination; and hardwoods (hornbeam, oak, and so on) for their aesthetic value, for wildlife, and because they steadily increase in value. Martin Wolfe says that 'all agriculture should be conceived as an exercise in agroforestry' and the more I think about it, the more this seems to me to be true. Outstanding too in Britain is Martin Crawford who combines forestry of a complex kind with horticulture, to produce a 'forest garden'. Both are well worth looking up on Google; and there are many other initiatives worldwide. In general, everyone benefits. The trees bring up nutrients from below and fertilize the crops. They provide shelter and browse (tree leaves) for livestock, which benefit enormously (in the tropics, cattle raised under trees may increase their milk-yield by up to 20 per cent); and so on.

Finally, it is worth thinking far more than we commonly do about aquaculture—ranging from carp in ponds (catfish or tilapia or whatever depending on climate) to the cultivation of the marine shallows that seem bound to reappear as global warming strikes and sea-levels rise. Needless to say, very little formal research is being done on this.

In short: farms that are designed with sound biology in mind—with respect for the physical needs of human beings, and of the crops and livestock, and the restraints of landscape and climate produce: plenty of plants, some but not much livestock, and great variety.

And here lies a wondrous but obvious serendipity: that the output of farms that march to the drum of sound biology exactly matches the nutritional needs of human beings as defined by modern nutritional science: *Plenty of plants, not much meat, and maximum variety.*

Yet, you will very properly protest, food isn't just a matter of nutrition. Food is about flavour, texture—gastronomy; and gastronomy is at the heart of all cultures. People in Britain in World War II were well-nourished, measured objectively, but they felt deprived nonetheless and rushed to embrace a more interesting diet as soon as rationing stopped in the 1950s. Laboratory rats are impeccably nourished on patent laboratory rat-feed but that doesn't mean they are happy—and besides, people are not rats. Mere nourishment in short, mere sustainability, aren't enough.

Indeed. This brings us to the second great serendipity:

The future belongs to the gourmet

Great chefs are extremely well paid these days, and very properly. They cook some wonderful things and generally speaking the modern chefs stress the things that matter: fine, fresh ingredients, prepared as simply as possible (although as Albert Einstein said in a somewhat different context, 'but no simpler'). Great chefs also emphasize that the very finest cuisine, all the world over, is rooted in traditional cooking.

And what are the basic ingredients of traditional cooking, all the world over? *Plenty of plants, not much meat, and maximum variety.*

In short, we can't lose. Farms that are designed to feed people forever—deliberately tailored to conform to the bedrock principles of human, animal, and plant physiology, and to the demands of ecology—produce exactly the right foods in the right proportions as recommended by modern nutritionists; and these in turn are precisely what is required to produce the world's finest cooking. It would indeed be easier to cater for a world full of vegans than a world full of hamburger addicts. But it is easiest of all to cater for people who really care about food. The future, indeed, belongs to the gourmet.

You don't have to be rich to be a gourmet. Chefs (whether great or not) like to charge fancy prices for what is sometimes called 'haute cuisine'. But all the greatest cooking, as all the truly great chefs acknowledge, is rooted in peasant cooking. Peasants, almost by definition, are not rich. But they do have access to good, basic, traditional farming (and usually, of course, were farmers themselves). All serious cooks need is plenty of staples, a mass as various as possible of other plants in season—leaves, fruits, roots—and whatever meat, eggs, milk and occasional fish as may come their way, and they can live as well as any royalty. The idea that the modern commercial diet of animal fat or hydrogenated palm oil, salt, sugar, and miscellaneous additives is cheap and delicious is just another lie. We can't all be farmers, but we can all be serious cooks. I have seen women cooking beautifully in old Bombay although they lived with their families on the street: a little tower of nesting brass pots with a few burning sticks beneath. Apartments are being built in London these days without kitchens. Since the world is run by idiots, it is really not surprising that we are in such a mess. But they are cunning idiots. They know how to disempower, and stay in charge.

For instance: the cooking of France is properly acknowledged to be among the finest in the world—and the French, traditionally, both rich and poor, derived at least half their calories from bread (but what bread!). Provençal cooking is rich in beans. Traditional Italian cuisine, which at least vies with French, is based on pasta and beans (again the theme of cereal and pulse). The hugely various cuisines of China and India are rightly acknowledged as among the world's finest. In both, at least in the more tropical south, the diet consists largely of rice—tricked out merely with whatever vegetables are around, and bits of whatever animals and fish happen to be around at the time, and with fermented foods such as pickles and, in China, with soy sauce, and in Japan with miso. Turkish cooking can border on the miraculous: banquets created from wheat (cracked), olive oil, almonds, mint, honey, whatever fish happen to have been pulled from the shore and perhaps some goat, if one happens to have died that week (I exaggerate, but not much). Even in northern Europe, which seems so meat-orientated (northern Europe is richer than most, and has a lot of grass and hills, and it is sometimes hard to supply fresh vegetables year round) the traditional cuisines are

still for the most part firmly rooted in plants. Bread again abounds—
especially before potatoes became widespread, in the 18th century:
Britons who ate well were said to be 'stout trenchermen', where the
'trencher' was the flat round loaf that accompanied every main meal
and indeed could serve as a plate. Stews, traditionally, are packed
with cabbage and turnips and much if not most of the calories comes
from dumplings. Wasn't it all grossly fattening, you might ask? Well,
there were fat people in olden times but obesity in general was not
a problem. It was seen only among the rich and the conspicuously
self-indulgent, and mercilessly lampooned. It was not universal as it
has become. Traditional diets are high in fibre (staples, vegetables)
and low in fat: dumplings are made with suet, but no one ate them
every day. The quantities were great in time of plenty but although
rich in flavour they were dilute in calories.

Taboos on meat—no pork, no beef, no horsemeat, no kids seethed
in their mother's milk—are generally economic in origin, though
they are typically couched in religious terms. But in general, people
who eat meat at all eat a wide variety: whatever is going. (Bushmeat
is not a good idea, however: the hunting of it spreads infection (both
ways) and leads to extinction as the beasts are caught that are easiest to catch, irrespective of esculence or rarity. Even the beautiful
and rare hyacinthine macaw is threatened by hunting, though it has
less meat on it than a quail). But traditional cooking does make use
of all parts of the beast—and some of the finest meals I have had
even in gourmet Italy were of tripe (the stomach and other intestine,
usually but not necessarily of cattle). Try buying tripe in a modern
supermarket. In traditional cooking, meat is the centrepiece only on
feast days—Christmas, Thanksgiving, St Bernadette's. Sunday, traditionally, was a mini-feast day, centred on 'the roast'. But in normal
times meat serves only as garnish or stock. Once a good Italian cook
has a good stock (chicken bones or fish heads are a fine start) it's all
over bar the shouting.

Contrast, briefly, the diet as provided by the modern food industry. High in meat, fat, salt, sugar; massively calorific but not satisfy-
ing—not least because deficient in micronutrients; rich in artifices—
additives—that add colour, mask flavour, and act as preservatives to

make provender look fresh that in truth may have hung about for weeks or months; each additive justified (if at all) by complaisant scientists on the grounds that, when given alone, it has so far failed to wreak any consistently measurable havoc among laboratory rats. No wonder poor kids whose mothers have not been taught how to cook and live on the nonsense churned out by the modern food industry find it hard to concentrate, and take to twocking cars. They are out of their heads: overfed yet malnourished; brains addled by a non-stop deluge of chemical junk. And the world's richest and most powerful governments stand by and watch it happen, and have lunch with the chief executives of the companies that make the junk (though careful to avoid the junk themselves) and then rush back to their respective parliaments to make excuses for them. It is disgusting. But the gaff is blown. The game is up. We have to run our affairs better than this; and since governments and the corporates they serve have proved so irresponsible, we (humanity) just have to do it ourselves, just as we have done for the past 10,000 years. This is the nettle that has to be grasped.

I will come back to this. First there is more ground to be laid. Enlightened agriculture, as is clear, is far more complicated than the modern kind—which simply grows the same crop over the biggest possible area, applying fertilizer and herbicide and pesticide according to the calendar (as opposed to the weather or the condition of the soil or actual state of the putative pests), following the manufacturers' instructions. Farming by numbers it used to be called, derisorily, before it became the norm. Enlightened agriculture is what used simply to be called good husbandry. It requires attention to detail. It requires good farmers, in short, and plenty of them. It cannot be practiced by one worker on a thousand hectares, as is now the ambition. Neither, as is often the current reality, can enlightened farming be achieved by one salaried worker and a score or so of immigrant transients of conveniently dubious legal standing (who's counting? Who cares?) to fill in the cracks. Good farmers are essential; people who understand the land, and crops, and livestock, and give a damn. Farmers in turn need back-up. Thus enlightened agriculture requires truly agrarian communities—the very thing that 'modern' governments (not modern at all in reality, as we will see) are seeking to eliminate.

In short: if we really care about our own future; if we really want to ensure that our grandchildren have enough to eat, and live in tolerable societies, and have other species to share the world with—and that their children and grandchildren can in turn enjoy the privileges of this astonishing Earth—then we need to acknowledge that the future economy of the world needs to be agrarian. Behind Enlightened Agriculture lies The New Agrarianism.

Before we move on, though, a postscript is called for.

Postscript:
Enlightened Agriculture and organic farming

You may well be wondering at this point how Enlightened Agriculture as described here differs from organic farming. Not much, is the short answer. But there are some important distinctions.

In general, no two farms are exactly alike and farming this past 10,000 years has surely manifested in many millions of different ways. But all of them can, at least roughly, be placed in one of three categories.

The first—traditional farms—make use of what there is. They do not make use of high technologies—mechanical power and artificial fertilizers or pesticides for the simple reason that until the 19th century they had not been invented, and they did not become commonplace until well into the 20th century. So if we define 'organic farming' simply as farming that does not partake of industrial chemistry, we could say that all farming was organic at least until the 19th century and most was organic, in this basic sense, until well into the 20th. The world population when large-scale farming first began around 10,000 years ago is estimated at a mere 10 million. Since numbers were approaching three billion by the 1930s, when high-tech farming first became widespread, we can see how successful craft-based, traditional farming has been. It produced a three-hundred fold increase in human numbers since hunter-gathering days—and has contributed a great deal to the further increase, since the 1930s, when the population has doubled again. It simply isn't true, as some zealots for modernity seem to think, that farming was floundering until science and high tech came on the scene. In truth, agricultural science has achieved the successes it has only because it had such a firm—traditional—base to build on.

The second form of farming is the industrialized kind, which makes maximum use of mechanical power and industrial chemistry; and although industrial farming is the Johnny-come-lately, it is already commonly called 'conventional farming'. It is conventional, however, only insofar as it makes use of western methods, and is geared to the western, industrial economy.

The third form is modern organic farming. It is like traditional farming insofar as it makes no use of industrial chemistry (or at least, makes only minimal use)—but the modern organic farmer actively rejects the industrial methods: it's not that they are not available. Organic farms also tend to be more traditional in structure than industrial farms: more craft-based, and more labour intensive; and organic farmers apply 'tender loving care' as a matter of philosophy. So in general ways organic farms have important features in common with traditional farms—much more than with industrialized farms. Yet it is wrong to imagine that modern organic farms are merely traditional, or are in any sense old-fashioned. They make tremendous use of modern science, often of the most intricate kind, to ensure for example that the soil is maintained in the best possible 'heart'—finest texture, highest fertility, high organic content; and to explore means of containing pests by 'biological' means, for example by encouraging natural predators into the crops. To a large extent the science of organic farming is ecology—and ecology is not an exercise in airy-fairyness, but is the most intricate of all the biological sciences. Organic farming is not an exercise in nostalgia, in short. It makes use of the most refined of all the biological sciences. The pity is that so little is spent on organic agricultural research. The lion's share of research money, and then some more, is spent on the comparative crudeness of 'conventional' farming, and in particular on its latest scion, biotech. But then, conventional farms can more easily be designed to generate cash, so they have more to spend.

Enlightened agriculture as I envisage it is very like modern organic farming. Indeed if modern organic farming became the norm, then I would be happy to acknowledge that enlightened agriculture had arrived. Yet enlightened agriculture does begin from a slightly different ideological base. Lady Eve Balfour, who founded Britain's Soil Association in the 1940s emphasized above all the need to take care of the soil: 'Take care of the soil and the crops will take care of themselves'. Indeed. No argument. But although she and the other 19th and 20th century philosophers and agriculturalists who lent their ideas and scholarship to the early organic movement included many with advanced social conscience, the organic movement was not founded specifically to provide good food for everyone forever. It could do this, probably, if well applied. But that was not its specific agenda. It is, however, the prime agenda, from the outset, of Enlightened Agriculture.

You may feel this is just a quibble, but it has practical consequences. Notably, the rules of modern organic farming banish a great many technologies absolutely, and as a matter of principle, including artificial fertilizers, pesticides, and of course genetic engineering. I would not myself ban any technology *a priori*, on first principles. Sometimes artificial fertilizers made by industrial processes can give a crop just the boost it needs to make full use of transient sunshine or rain. Sometimes particularly recalcitrant pests can be controlled most efficiently, and with least collateral damage to other wild creatures, with pesticides that could well be on the black list. Later I will discuss some applications of genetic engineering that seem to be benign—that could truly make like easier for traditional communities who wish to retain their own ways of life. The trouble, I will argue, does not lie with the technology itself, but with the economic framework in which it is now obliged to operate, which ensures that these highest of technologists are deployed primarily or even exclusively by corporates, who in turn work hand-in-gloves with powerful governments, so that in practice they become agents of social and political control—obliterating the ways of life that they could be abetting.

In short, Enlightened Agriculture would allow itself to be more catholic in its choice of technology, than organic farming is. Even so, I recognize that the high technologies that the organic farmers eschew have in practice become agents of top-down governmental control; and that in this crude political world of ours the only practical way to prevent a top-down takeover is to ban these technologies all together. Thus, organic farming has taken on the mantle of Enlightened Agriculture by default. As things stand, in this crude and aggressive world, the 'organic' label serves at least in part to demonstrate that the food in question has not been produced by means that are beyond the pale. If and when general awareness is raised, and only then, will it become possible to relax the rules without re-opening the floodgates to the present horrors of wall-to-wall monoculture and factory livestock.

But finally, and very importantly, we can already see that the 'organic' label, defined in its present forms, is capable of serious abuse. In Britain we can buy 'organic' apples from New Zealand, which is as far from Britain as it is possible to get without leaving the Earth. The main street of a small town near me is often blocked by a vast truck, as big as a warship, bearing organic produce from several counties. Organic crops more and more are grown as monocultures, on the vast scale. In short, organic farming is becoming industrialized just as the 'conventional' kind already has been—with the same top-down control. It is important, therefore, *not* to define Enlightened Agriculture purely in terms of one particular technical approach. Agriculture becomes truly enlightened only when it keeps all the balls in the air—biological, social, moral—with the general aim of creating a world that is good for everyone forever, and for other creatures too. Unfortunately, therefore, as things are, enlightened agriculture cannot simply sneak in behind the skirts of organic farming. It overlaps the organic movement very considerably, and some organic farmers are among the most enlightened of all and are indeed exemplars for the whole world. But still, Enlightened Agriculture must have its own identity.

So where have we gone wrong?

In principle, it really should not be difficult to supply everyone who is ever likely to be born with great food, forever; and to do so without wiping out other creatures, and generally wrecking the fabric of the Earth.

In reality, present day agriculture is not directly geared to human wellbeing, and takes virtually no account of biological reality. Instead, it is designed to make money, in the apparent belief that the maximization of disposable wealth is both necessary and sufficient. How this works, why it is so destructive, and how this perverse state of affairs came about, is discussed in the next two chapters.

Then I will revert to a positive vein and discuss what we can do to put things right).

CHAPTER 4

The rot sets in: farming for money

We are failing, miserably, to feed ourselves properly. Along the way, we cause huge collateral misery while wrecking the fabric of the world itself. If we go on as we are then life will be impossible for own children and grandchildren. Why are we behaving so perversely?

The powers-that-be are in charge (by definition) and I have often asked in rhetorical vein, are they stupid, or are they wicked? Actually the question is not quite rhetorical, because some people in high places are remarkably ill-informed and demonstrably stupid, and are seriously wicked when judged by what seem to me to be reasonable standards. Indeed, the logistics of power to a significant extent favours wickedness in the highest places because the people who are most likely to acquire the most power are the ones who are most focused on power; and the desire for personal power seems largely incompatible with the primary virtues of respect for others, and of personal humility.

But many rich and powerful people are neither stupid nor wicked. Rich and powerful people include some of the most intelligent of all and some of the best: people who really do want the world to be a better place, and seek to benefit humanity as a whole. Some of them are renowned historical figures—the kind generically known as philanthropists. Such people still exist and I know some of them personally: social entrepreneurs who set up businesses (or maintain businesses that bring little profit) specifically to benefit their own societies. I have seen this in particular in India among people from both a mercantile and a Hindu tradition. In the West the Quakers, steeped in Christian morality, have been serious commercial players—and of course you don't have to be either a Hindu or a

Christian to be humanitarian. So the idea that wealth and power necessarily reflect stupidity and wickedness is just plain wrong.

So the fault does not lie primarily with wickedness, or with stupidity. It lies with error. We have contrived by degrees to create a world economic system that is bad for humanity in general and disastrous for agriculture in particular—the thing we absolutely have to get right. How come?

What's gone wrong?

To people brought up in the Cold War—which must include most people reading this since the Cold War officially ended only in 1989—the world's economy is clearly divided into Communist and capitalist. The West is generally conceived to be capitalist, and those who feel that the present western economy is not what the world needs, are still liable to be called 'Commies', and banned from serious further discourse.

In truth, although the Communist party still rules in China, and China is rapidly becoming the world's biggest economy, the kind of economics that Communism traditionally embraced is now rare. In this, as first envisaged by Karl Marx, the people at large own 'the means of production'. People-at-large in reality means the state; so the economy is centrally controlled. Only a few modern countries adhere to this model, such as Cuba and North Korea. The Communist party is still big in Russia and is the ruling party in China but both preside over economies that are unmistakably capitalist.

Many conclude from this that the ideological war is over. Indeed, all the world's economies—all except those eccentrics that have kept themselves to themselves or have been shunned—subscribe to the global free market, presided over by the World Trade Organization, based in Geneva. Capitalism has won, and that is the end of it. Some observers, including many in the highest places, heave a huge sigh of relief. All we have to do now, they argue, is to get on and make global capitalism work. The world is now united—at last! The free market delivers the goods that we all need, with wondrous efficiency. For good measure, it has a firm moral base. After all, traders can succeed only by supplying what consumers will buy, so consumers must be in the driving seat. Since everyone is a consumer, the system is innately democratic. Who could ask for more? Anyone who isn't an enthusiastic capitalist these days must be an idiot, or (as George W Bush put the matter), 'evil'. Doubters must be the enemies of democracy, and world unity, and therefore the enemies of humankind itself.

What this simple-minded but alarmingly common view of the world significantly fails to register is that there is a huge, deep, ideological and practical division within capitalism itself. On the one hand we have the global, allegedly free market, which now prevails. On the other hand, we have capitalism as envisaged, and espoused, by the founders of the modern United States—Ben Franklin, George Washington, Thomas Jefferson, James Madison and the rest—at the end of the 18th century and the beginning of the 19th. The difference between the two capitalist models is almost as profound as the difference between capitalism as a whole, and the centralized economies of the Marxists. People like me who feel that the global free market in its present form is a disaster are not necessarily 'Commies', or religious 'fanatics', or hippies or weirdos. On the contrary, I see myself as a good Jeffersonian. The United States was the greatest social experiment ever undertaken, breathtaking in brilliance and moral sure-footedness, and if only the US had continued as it began, the world would now be a very different and a far better place. I hate the present system—we have to stand up to it—but in hating it, I claim to be a better capitalist than its modern practitioners.

In truth, there seems to be no universally agreed definition of 'capitalism'—all the world's biggest concepts prove remarkably elusive when you look at them closely. But I argue, as many do, that capitalism is really about free trade, markets, and personal ownership, and as such it seems to be as old as humankind. Neanderthals clearly traded in stone tools, often over long distances; and they may have traded in a great deal else besides, of which there is now no trace. Trading might almost be seen as the defining characteristic of our species. It is indeed 'natural'. Being natural does not make it morally right. But it does make it easy to live with.

In the beginning

It is impossible to say when modern capitalism really began—there were money-changers in the Bible, and Europe's Renaissance was financed by Italian bankers. But a key player, beyond doubt, was Adam Smith: twin pillar, along with David Hume, of the Scottish Enlightenment. In a series of essays, but particularly in *The Wealth of Nations* of 1776, he explained why the free market could indeed meet the needs and desires of humanity. In a well-tempered market there should be many different traders, all competing for customers. The customers would be free to choose between them. Traders who tried to palm off inferior goods, or cheated, would soon be found out. Then the customers would go elsewhere, and the cheats would go out of business. Thus, said Smith, an 'invisible hand' would ensure that honesty and justice prevailed. In other words, each individual player in the market, whether trader or customer, merely had to do his or her own thing and, as if by magic, an efficient, honest society would result. By contrast, said Smith, if people set out consciously to design an agreeable society by imposing some particular vision upon it (as, for example, various religious leaders were wont to do) then the result could be anything but agreeable.

Adam Smith's model is alluring and in principle it surely works. But he hedged his thesis with caveats. First, he was a moral philosopher before he was an economist, and he did not envisage that the free market was society's only driver. He imagined that the individuals who took part in the market were, at least to some extent, moral beings: that they were possessed of what in his *Theory of Moral Sentiments* he speaks of 'natural sympathy'. For example, a trader was perfectly entitled to shout more loudly than his rivals. But he could not murder them. The market overall was subject to the law of the land, which in turn was intended to reflect the general moral beliefs of the people. Smith recognized too that the market, as he en-visaged it, was an ideal—it could never quite be realized in practice. The invisible hand could be relied upon to dispense justice only if there was an infinite number of traders, competing on level terms; and an infinite number of consumers who each had perfect access to all the traders, and perfect knowledge of what was going on. If any trader had a monopoly, or groups of traders—or consumers—ganged together to form cartels to put pressure on the rest, or if in-formation was concealed or misrepresented, then the invisible hand could not work its magic. The market would simply be dominated by the strongest players for their own particular benefit.

Jefferson and his fellow founders set out to create a country that was, some might say, a utopia: except that 'utopia' means 'no-where' and is by its nature imaginary, while the new United States was wonderfully real. The founders listed what they thought was desirable. Democracy was the sine qua non: as Abraham Lincoln put the matter a few decades later, government 'by the people, of the people, and for the people'. The founders wanted individual people to be free because freedom is an essential prerequisite of personal fulfillment. They wanted social justice, for as they spelled out in the Declaration of Independence of 1776, '...all men are created equal'. They wanted efficiency, because the antithesis of efficiency is waste, and waste is a sin. They knew full well that these desiderata are to some extent in conflict. Absolute personal freedom implies action without restraint which is socially catastrophic. Democracy and economic efficiency don't necessarily make easy bedfellows. None-theless they felt that the market economy as conceived by Adam Smith would serve their needs. So they founded the world's first, consciously-designed democratic republic, and it was (by most defi-nitions) capitalist.

But the founders' vision has been horribly betrayed. Jefferson must be spinning in his grave. Enthusiasts for the global free market are fond of citing Adam Smith, the austere, Enlightenment Scots-man. But they are almost as far removed from Smith as Marx was.

The end of the invisible hand

Since the founders' day there have been three key changes.

First, the market as a whole has been taken over, and is now largely controlled, by corporates. Even worse—the coup de grâce—the world's most powerful governments now depend on those corporates. In the US, no presidential candidate can get a sniff of power without corporate wealth behind him. Britain's New Labour party was anxious since before it first came to power in 1997 to assure the city—the corporates—that it was on their side; that it would do nothing to inhibit them. To a significant extent, the world's most powerful governments are extensions of the corporate boardroom.

'Ordinary' companies, by and large, are each dedicated to some particular métier. Some make furniture, some make pickles, and so on. They need to make a profit—take in more money than they spend. But the profit is a means to an end. The end is to stay in business, so they can make more sideboards or piccalilli. Corporates are very big companies, or conglomerates of companies, that are not necessarily dedicated to any particular activity or product. In principle they might make furniture *and* pickles, and a great deal else besides, shifting investment from one to another according to what is most profitable. Corporates are, in fact, engines for generating money. That does not make them innately bad. But it certainly makes them powerful—in money, of course, but also politically, because governments need money.

Jefferson and his fellow founders knew all about corporates. The Boston Tea Party of 1773, a key event in the build-up to independence, was a protest against the British-based and all-powerful East India Company, which in that particular instance was using its economic and political muscle to bully small American tea traders out of business. Jefferson also knew that in a free market, corporates are bound to arise. There is no innate mechanism within the market to prevent companies growing bigger, or from forming conglomerates. Furthermore, the bigger they got the more they could promote their own growth since they could use their enormous buying power to drive hard bargains and to undercut rivals. As the adage has it, money goes to money. So Jefferson and Madison in particular framed laws to restrict the power of corporates. Corporates could not, the law said, extend their influence beyond their own state. They had to renew their licences every year. They were kept on a very right rein, by the democratically elected government.

But at the end of the 19th century, as every American law student learns, the law that constrained the corporates was overturned. In fact, as Thom Hartmann admirably explains in *Unequal Protection: The Rise of Corporate Dominance and the Theft of Human Rights* (Rodale Books, Emmaus, PA, 2004), the law was not overturned. The court case in which the overturning allegedly took place was simply misreported. But it was widely perceived that the law had been overturned and what was perceived to have happened, but didn't, in one courtroom about 130 years ago, has changed the course of the world. The liberation of the corporates was, perhaps, the most important single event of the 19th century, or indeed of the modern world. All the world's most powerful governments are now beholden to corporates and so, of course, is the global market. But a market with only a few giant players is very different indeed from the market that Adam Smith envisaged, with a virtual infinity of small players, none of whom had any particular influence on the whole. The modern global economy is not the dynamic, restless interplay of infinite components that Smith envisaged. It is a ponderous clash of titans. In such a system, the invisible hand that is supposed to create social justice, does not come into play.

The second huge shift has been the rise of finance capitalism. The idea has grown—it has always been around—that money can buy anything. As Bob Geldof recently put the matter, if the people of Niger had money, they could buy food. They were starving only because they lacked money. If this is true, then it seems to follow that the greater the pile of money, the better. The creation and the generation of wealth—almost by whatever means—is thus justified on moral grounds. After all, the more money you have, the more good you can do; and if you have no money, you cannot do any good at all. Anthony Trollope summarized this notion in *The Way*

We Live Now (1875). His fictional banker, Melmotte, tells his gullible, potential investors:

> These are great times and I am proud to be an Englishman
> in these times! What is the engine of this world? Profit.
> Gentlemen it is your duty to make yourself rich!

Trollope intended this as parody, and Melmotte is an obvious villain. But his stated philosophy seems now to be taken for granted.

The moral excuse for extreme personal wealth is provided by the notion of 'trickle down': only a few may be rich today, but the wealth of the few must spread to the many. Up to a point this is true. Rich people can employ poor people, and entrepreneurs who are truly socially inspired can create fine industries that give rise to and support entire communities. There are countless examples.

But wealth doesn't necessarily 'trickle down'. For century after century, the rich may stay rich and the poor stay poor—the rich using their power to ensure that they maintain their ascendancy. As economists at the merchant bankers Goldman Sachs recently put the matter, 'The most important contributor to higher profit margins over the past five years has been a decline in labor's share of national income.' The rich grow richer and the poor grow poorer not only in all those Third World countries which the rich countries like to believe are 'corrupt', but in the US itself, the world leader of the new economic order. Thom Hartmann records in *What Would Jefferson Do?* (Three Rivers Press, New York, 2004) that since 1981, when Ronald Reagan became president, the USA has grown richer and richer while the real income of the middle class has declined by 10 per cent and the minimum wage of the poorest people has fallen by 17 per cent. Eighty per cent of American homeowners of low and moderate income now spend more than half their income on housing, and half of the ever-spiralling tally of bankruptcies are brought about by medical bills (and how many of these bills result from the diet? Diabetes for instance can be very expensive, leading as it does to horrible circulatory problems and blindness). In Britain, my children's generation is similarly obsessed, perforce, with putting a roof over their heads (and with paying off their student loans). I recall a world-weary comment from George Orwell from the 1930s, that 'The average Englishman owns nothing—except perhaps a house'. Only now can we see the unintended irony of his comment.

At the time of writing (May 2010) Britain has a new government—the first coalition since World War II. It remains to be seen what they will do with agriculture. But since neither of the two parties in the coalition—the Conservatives and the Liberal Democrats—mentioned agriculture in their election manifestos, it seems likely right now that they will simply continue the policies of New Labour, which have prevailed since 1997. Tony Blair and Gordon Brown, Prime Minister and Chancellor during most of New Labour, evidently had tremendous faith in 'trickle down'. Evidently they believed that salvation for African countries lies with foreign companies (notably corporates) setting up shop within their boundaries, and making money. Somehow, the wealth created is supposed to bring general benefit. In a recent lecture at Oxford a member of Britain's House of Lords assured us that the spanking new Manhattan skyline of Nairobi, its new business centre, is the harbinger of Africa's great future. It reminded me rather of Shelley's 'Ozymandias', a monument of anachronistic vainglory. I have heard African leaders publicly praying that no one discovers oil in their country. Oil brings untold riches. But most of the people in most oil-rich countries have not noticeably benefited at all. Indeed, they often have the most vicious regimes of all.

But such is the emphasis on wealth per se, that governments nowadays measure their own success in it: specifically in terms of GDP—gross domestic product. Increase in GDP is called 'economic growth'. Nations that are 'growing' fastest are deemed to be the most successful, and those with little or no growth are perceived as lame ducks or even as 'failed states'. Failed states are ripe for intervention, or so the rich like to think. It would be doing them a favour to take them over.

Yet John Maynard Keynes, no less, warned that GDP has very little to do with wellbeing. Wellbeing is not what GDP is intended to measure. For one thing, any kind of activity that makes money is deemed to contribute to GDP. The destruction of New Orleans by hurricane Katrina in August 2005 could well contribute in net to America's GDP because the construction industry is having a field day putting it together again (or would be, if anyone was prepared to pay). War is extremely lucrative, which is one reason why there is so much of it. Crime in the US in particular is a huge industry: all those prisons, prison officers, policemen, lawyers, clerks, cleaners, drivers, and manufacturers of safes, burglar alarms, guns, truncheons, cop cars and goodness knows what contribute wonderfully to GDP. It is a tremendous wheeze, economically speaking, to put so many people in prison (more, in the US, than are working full-time on the land). Mayhem, war, and crime hardly contribute to human wellbeing, so most sane people would surely agree. But they can be awfully good for the GDP and GDP—'growth'—dominates all political agenda.

There is worse. One of the best and easiest ways to make money these days is simply to manipulate money itself. This is what 'finance capitalism' really implies. Britain seems to have 'out-sourced' or sold off most of its industry—the pursuits that actually produce stuff—and is most proud, these days, of its 'financial services', aka 'the City' run by bankers and brokers of various kinds. These people do not actually produce anything. They merely move money from one pile to another, and skim a little off as it passes through. The money, these days, does not actually exist. It is merely deemed to exist. The enormous sums that we now hear bandied—billions or even trillions of dollars, or pounds, or euros—are just figures in a computer and most of them are noughts.

The source of this notional money is the future. Since the global collapse things have tightened up, but before the collapse anyone who was not obviously mad or in a coma could borrow money beyond their wildest dreams. The only condition was that they had to pay it back with compound interest. Compound interest ensures that borrowers pay back several times what they borrow even in a short time—and if they fail to keep up the payments then the debt goes on increasing. The money owed to the lender is deemed to be money that they in fact own, so both the borrower (who has access to the money lent) and the lender (who is paid interest and expects to receive several times what was paid out) are deemed to be richer. Such debt economies give the illusion of wealth—a few years ago we could all borrow enough to buy a Rolls Royce or Lamborghini—but the wealth is rooted in nothing at all, except a vague hope that it will be forthcoming in the future, and the whole house of cards collapses as soon as people begin to see how illusory the whole thing is. Which it has now done.

Meanwhile, as the German biologist-turned economist Margrit Kennedy has been pointing out for some decades, the need to borrow money and to pay compound interest on the loan ensures that most people in modern societies are in net deficit. They might make a little from the interest they get from their pension schemes or whatever; and the money they make is derived from the interest on loans made to other people. But most of us are also paying compound interest on our own debts. You may feel this is not true—you have paid your mortgage and have nothing on HP and therefore have no debts. Thus a greengrocer who sells you your Brussels sprouts will be paying a mortgage for his shop—and the interest on his mortgage must be reflected in the price he charges for his sprouts, or he goes out of business. Everyone else involved in producing and selling sprouts will be in debt too, for something or other. So some of the sprout money goes to the farmer (not much), and some goes to the distributor, and some to the greengrocer—and a very fair slice goes to the banks, who have lent money to the farmer, the distributor, and the greengrocer, and expect to be paid back, several times over.

In practice, in a typical modern society, 80 per cent of the people are in net deficit; 10 per cent are in a neutral state—income from lending balancing the interest paid; and 10 per cent are in net profit. Thus there is a net flow of money from 80 per cent of the people to the richest 10 per cent. In 2004, in Germany, this net flow amounted to about one billion euros *per day*. Thus in the present kind of economy the discrepancy between rich and poor is bound to go on growing, even if the poor did not actually get poorer (which in practice is very much the case). Germany, too, we might note, is among the best organized and probably among the least corrupt of countries. In the United States, the systematized flow of wealth from the poor to the rich, combined with America's own particular brand of neoliberal ruthlessness has brought us to the point where the richest one per cent own more than the bottom 95 per cent. 'The bottom 95' per cent is an extraordinary expression. It means 'most of the people'. Indeed the people of the US (and most of us elsewhere, too) live the lives of villagers in the books of our childhood—perpetually oppressed and impoverished by the giant who lives on the hill. For 'giant' these days read 'corporates, banks, and the governments who compete to support them'. Yet the US was established expressly as the world's first state dedicated from the outset to justice and equality. The Founding Fathers must be spinning in their graves.

All this would not be quite as hideous if the money that is generated by these extraordinary means had no real buying power. It isn't 'real', after all. But, anomalously and absurdly, all this hypothetical money can be translated at any time into real goods. Thus the people who are among the net recipients of wealth can buy out the rest of us—using our own money to do it, which we created by our industry. And so they do. So it is, for example, that the agriculture of Britain and the US, which to many worldwide are seen as the exemplar, depends to a huge extent on the whims of the rich, who might, for example, be perfectly content to take land out of production and graze their daughters' ponies instead. In some English counties, 'horsey-culture' occupies much of the landscape. The richest people of all the world over either inherited their wealth, perhaps originally from some distant ancestor who performed some favour for some medieval king, or became extremely rich simply by shuffling other people's money.

Overall, finance capitalism leaves us with a huge, ludicrous, and potentially lethal problem. For the actions and strategies of the present world are geared to an abstraction—the abstraction of money. With remarkable speed, even at modest interest rates, small loans turn into sums that could, on paper, buy half of Europe. Eventually, compounding interest on even the smallest loans leads us to infinity. But although this money is just a line on a piece of paper, in practice it can be turned into real things—yachts, mansions, forests, farms, what you will. Yet the real world, where we all live, is all too obviously finite. The wealth that people are positively encouraged to accumulate, and which in practice can be used to indulge almost any whim, is already theoretically sufficient enough to buy the world several times over. Yet in reality, this is obvious nonsense. An economy that takes no serious account of physical reality is all immensely dangerous. But this is the lunacy we live with, and are apparently beholden to. The longer we persist with it, the deeper the hole we will dig ourselves into.

In truth, the present economy does have some advantages. It is good that people who want to do things and seem able to do them should be able to borrow money so that they can get on with them, and not have to go to some aristocratic patron, cap in hand, as Columbus did, or Beethoven, or anyone in the past who was not rich already. It has often been suggested too—not least by bankers—that if only the people at large owned the banks and ensured that no one, not even the bankers, should be ludicrously rich, them all could be well. Neither should we assume that the corporates are bad a priori, even though some of them behave very badly indeed. There clearly are some corporates that do more good than harm. The reasons why the bad ones are so bad need to be carefully identified (which so far as I know, is not happening). Overall, the globalized economy may be good for some purposes.

But I am content to let others, with greater expertise, argue these general points. I want merely to point out that whatever its perceived advantages, the present economy, dominated by the globalized clash of corporates and the speculations of banks, and by governments who depend on both, is disastrous for agriculture. But agriculture is the thing we have to get right.

'Agriculture is just a business like any other'

I first became aware of the turn that the economy was taking in the 1970s when I worked for the British farming magazine *Farmer's Weekly*. It was then that I first heard the chill phrase, 'Agriculture is just a business like any other'.

Of course agriculture is a business. I dare say—stretching a point—that Cain and Abel thought of themselves as businessmen. They produced food, I imagine on their own initiative, and expected to sell it. That's business. Stalin tried to create agriculture run by 'workers' who merely toiled for the state, with no scope for individual initiative and no special reward for special effort, and largely failed. He would have failed even more disastrously if he had not, perhaps cannily, given the peasants at least some scope to do their own thing. And peasants, at least when they are allowed to be, are business people who expect to feed themselves but also to sell their surpluses for a profit.

Of course, too, business is to some extent competitive. There isn't room in the world for all the people who would like to make things or to trade, and although we can share out the opportunities by imposing quotas (which remain a very useful device) it is nonetheless good for everybody if there is at least some way of ensuring that people who are truly incompetent, lose out to people who do the job better. Otherwise, at best, the incompetent ones simply waste precious resources.

Yet no society throughout history that I can think of, has regarded its agriculture *simply* as a business. Always people at large and the powers-that-be have felt that farming is in various ways special. Most obviously, its output is vital to us all, and cannot be interrupted even for a few weeks. No other industry can claim as much, so convincingly. Yet the output of this vital industry is bound to vary from year to year, unpredictably, for reasons that are quite beyond human control—the greatest single reason being the vagaries of weather. Total wipe-out of crops or livestock is of course a disaster for everyone. But glut is bad news too, at least for the farmers, for it simply sends the price right down—so that very large yields, paradoxically, can force farmers out of business. Farmers are human beings too, and it seems unjust that they should go bust when their crops fail through no fault of their own; and perhaps even more unjust if they go bust just because, in a particular year, they produce *more* than society needs. In the long term, too, at least in traditional societies where farming had to be labour intensive because there were no big machines or industrial chemistry, it was in nobody's interests for farmers to be put out of work, because society at large all too obviously needed them.

So although farmers have commonly worked within a general atmosphere of free trade, most civilised and organised societies have manipulated the market to ensure that the farmers, who produced the food that all of us rely upon, stayed in business. Thus societies at least since classical times have evolved a whole series of sticks and carrots, checks and balances—quotas, tariffs, grants, support buying, incentive payments and so on—to ensure that farmers, although in principle free to do their own thing, in practice do the things that society wants them to do, and do not go out of business through no fault of their own. This in principle seems both just and sensible.

At the same time, competition has always been a fact of business and a fact of life—but not the only fact. Farmers have often formed all kinds of cooperatives, for example in creating various marketing boards. If cooperatives become cartels then this is bad for the consumers, and for the producers who are not in the cartel. But cooperatives in general can be of enormous help to everyone. Individual farmers in particular regions have traditionally competed with each other, not least in the agricultural shows, when each farmer tried to demonstrate that his cow or pig or sack of barley was better than his or her neighbour's. But equally, within farming communities that are truly worthy of the name, such competition was little more than friendly rivalry, each competitor spurring the others to greater effort. When the chips were down, as indeed in traditional societies they often were, neighbours helped each other. More broadly, in my days at *Farmer's Weekly*, I was always impressed by the freedom and generosity with which individual farmers discussed their methods and their successes with the world at large. In general, if they found a good way to do things, then they wanted others to share in it. Even in today's frenetically competitive atmosphere, I find that farmers are still more than happy to come together to discuss better ways of doing things, to everyone's benefit. The pity is that there are now so few, at least in Britain, that serious gatherings are harder and harder to arrange. Mercifully—another significant ray of sunshine—the internet is making it very easy to communicate. Indeed, many people have suggested in many contexts, the internet could yet be the saviour of humankind—in principle enabling everyone on Earth to communicate rapidly and fully with everyone else. Individually, human beings are deeply flawed. It's only when we put our heads together that we really come into our own. Unfortunately, some farmers don't have the time or the energy to log on at the end of a working day, and at least one I met recently simply couldn't afford to buy a computer sufficiently up-to-date to be useful. But we're getting there.

Nowadays, though, all-out competition is perceived as the prime and necessary virtue. The present British government, taking its lead from Margaret Thatcher's philosophy in the 1980s, is basing its entire policies in all spheres, including medicine and education, on the perceived need to compete. The very obvious fact that cooperation has its virtues too—most obviously it saves a great deal of fighting, which takes a huge amount of energy for no constructive purpose—has been written out of the act. Competition has become the order of the day, not because it works particularly well, but as a matter of dogma. The dogma dominates even though common sense and simple hawks-and-doves game theory show that societies that are essentially cooperative can most easily produce an outcome that is best for all; and also shows, contrariwise, that societies that indulge in all-out competition can *never* produce outcomes that are good for all but must always favour the hawks, and (though to a lesser extent) those who kow-tow to the hawks.

Our food supply is particularly badly hit by the new economics. The things that farmers need to do in order to stay financially afloat are absolutely at odds, diametrically opposed, to what needs to be done if we seriously care about the 6.8 billion people who are with us now, and the nine billion who will be here by 2050, and the other five to eight million species with whom we share this Earth; and if indeed we care about our own children. Not capitalism per se, but the modern form of it, is the greatest mistake that can be conceived. This is easily demonstrated.

How to be a successful capitalist—and why farming is different

To begin with, the aim of the universal money-game isn't simply to make money, but to generate profit: profit being the difference between the price received for the finished goods, and the cost of producing them in the first place. Profit *per se* is not of course bad. In essence profit is a way of keeping score. It is the obsessive desire to maximise profit without moral restraint, and to do so with maximum competitiveness so that those who are not so single-minded go to the wall, that is so destructive.

A very good business friend of mine (who had his own business, and taught in a business school) explained to me years ago that to make a profit—in any business—you have to do three things:

First: maximise turnover. The more you have to sell, the more money you can make. 'Pile 'em high and sell 'em cheap' was Michael Marks's adage, of Marks & Spencer. Although you shouldn't sell 'em too cheap, because of the second requirement. To whit:

Second: add value. Adding value means by and large that you begin with raw material, or something very like it, and then you turn it into a 'good' (as the economists have it) that somebody actually wants to buy.

Third: minimise costs. Pay as little as possible for the goods in the first place.

These three requirements are the bedrock. Kept within reasonable and moral bounds, they are fine. They are no more than common sense. But if you set out expressly to maximise profit, with no other end in view; if you are determined to be as ruthless as is necessary to achieve this maximisation; and if you operate within and contribute towards an atmosphere of to-the-death, all-against-all competition; then the world is in trouble. Specifically, this simplistic approach produces a system of farming, and an overall food supply chain, that seems expressly designed to ensure that humanity as a whole cannot be well fed, and in which vast numbers of people are bound to be treated unjustly, and other creatures are bound to go extinct, and the future in general is left entirely to hazard. Let us take the three prime requirements one by one: maximum turnover, maximum value-adding, and minimum costs and see how this pans out in the context of agriculture.

The trouble with growing too much

In the 1970s it looked for a time as if it was going to be well-nigh impossible to feed the world population of the time, which then stood at something over four billion. In particular, yields of cereal in India were simply too low. It should have been possible to increase those yields simply by adding artificial nitrogen fertiliser ('N'). But India in those days grew old-fashioned varieties of wheat which had very long stems—that is, they were tall, like the shoulder-height cereals of Breughel's paintings. When these varieties were given extra N, they simply grew even taller, and fell over, or 'lodged' as farmers say. But from the late 1960s, using breeding techniques that fell short of *bona fide* genetic engineering but still were very fancy indeed—involving direct transfer of chromosomes from plant to plant—breeders were able to produce a new range of 'semi-dwarf' varieties of wheat, with short stems. When these were plied with extra N, they didn't grow tall. They produced more grain. The semi-dwarf varieties caught on and now most wheat worldwide is dwarfed. Modern wheat often is hardly above knee-height. But the yields of grain, when the crop is heavily fertilised, are fabulous: three times what was common in the 1970s. Comparable semi-dwarfing genes were then introduced into rice, which vies with wheat as the world's most important cultivated crop of all. The development of semi-dwarf varieties, and the heavy fertilisation and irrigation (sometimes) that went with it, was 'the Green Revolution'. Its perpetrators received Nobel Prizes.

There was, and is, a lot wrong with the Green Revolution. For one thing it put a lot of farmers out of work, with hugely adverse consequences. It required continuing capital input, mainly for nitrogen fertiliser, so on the whole it achieved less than is desirable for the poorest farmers. But it did produce a lot more grain and at first sight, it looks like, and has often been presented as, an unequivocal victory for high tech. Before the Green Revolution, with old-fashioned varieties, people went hungry. In the immediate aftermath, for a time, India, China, and Mexico emerged as net grain exporters. Can't be bad, you might think.

But yield isn't everything. Context is all. It is good to grow a big crop, to be sure. But there is no point in this if the crop cannot be sold. If everyone achieves high yields there is glut. The market is flooded. The price falls. We have seen the truth and disaster of this in the world's coffee market these past few decades. People worldwide have been drinking coffee at least since the 17th century but recently it has become even more wildly popular. Traders operating on the global scale have wanted more and more. Spurred by the modern vogue for global competition they have encouraged farmers to grow more and more of it—not simply the traditional coffee growers in Brazil, Costa Rica, Mexico, Kenya and so on but in places that a few years ago had hardly heard of coffee, such as Vietnam and East Timor. Fair enough, you might think. Except that too much has been produced. Between the 1980s and the 1990s the price of coffee on the global market fell seven-fold. I have seen entire plantations of coffee on Brazilian hillsides abandoned, dying in the sun, because the farmers knew that it would cost more to harvest the crop (let alone to grow it in the first place) than they would get for it on the world market.

Zealots for global free trade driven by maximum competition seem to see nothing wrong with this. If a Brazilian farmer goes bust because a Vietnamese farmer can grow the crop more cheaply— well: that's life. 'The consumer', we are told, benefits from the new cheap price—although of course that is not true: coffee on the high street becomes more and more expensive. It's the traders who benefit; the corporates who organise the global market and the governments who are supported by corporate wealth.

Advocates of the modern, allegedly free global market insist that it is rooted in the ideas of Adam Smith. Yet in practice the modern global free market has perverted the vision of Adam Smith just as profoundly as the predominant economy of the modern United States as a whole has perverted the vision of Thomas Jefferson. In practice, the allegedly free global market—in all goods, but of course including those of farming—is orchestrated by the biggest and most powerful players in a kind of global dog-fight. Nobody does well out of a dog-fight—certainly not the dogs—except the organisers. Market zealots argue that the Brazilians' bad luck in the coffee market is the Vietnamese bonanza: swings and roundabouts; it all works out in the end. But this is just another lie. Some Vietnamese business people undoubtedly do well from their new industry but the farmers as a whole certainly do not. They can sell their coffee on the world market only insofar as they can undercut the Brazilians. So they must be prepared to work even harder, for even less money. Meanwhile the organisers of the dogfight swan around the world buying from the most desperate. Soon the Chinese seem likely to produce more coffee more cheaply than anyone else (the Chinese have every kind of climate and in principle can grow anything, and of course can invest heavily in start-up) and then—goodbye Vietnam. China has already swamped the world's textile market: Sri Lankan politicians have commented that the damage thus done to the Sri Lankan people far exceeds the destruction wrought by the 2005 tsunami (although Europe, which has economic and military muscle and so has the power to bend the global rules, has temporarily been able to keep its own textile industry afloat).

Under the present global free market, with every farmer exhorted to produce the maximum, there can never be stability again. As soon as some new agricultural enterprise is up and running, someone else, in some quite different place, with some temporary advantage—even cheaper labour is the usual one—will undercut them. Yet this system, in which only the most desperate can sell anything at all (unless they buck the system and are subsidised with taxpayers' money, as in the United States and Europe), is supposed to provide the route to universal wealth. It is obvious nonsense: either a horrible mistake, or the most hideous exercise in cynicism. I digress slightly, but the point is made. Maximisation of yield is not necessarily a good thing. In the short term it leads to glut, and glut is very bad for producers although it may well be turned to advantage by those who are organising the global fight.

Glut, however, is merely the short-term disadvantage. In the longer term, the urge to maximise yield can produce far more lasting damage. Thus, and in particular, African farmers traditionally have not sought to maximise yield because they know that this is not usually the priority. The African climate in general is immensely fickle (and with global warming will be more so). There are very good growing years, and very bad ones. What matters is not to produce vast crops in good years (leading to glut) but to guarantee sufficient yields— often quite low yields but still sufficient—in bad years. Good yields can be achieved in bad years with more technology—notably, by irrigation. Irrigation can be good, of course: the annual flooding of the Nile that features so graphically in the Old Testament was an infinitely renewable benison that provided traditional Egypt with one of the finest agricultural systems the world has seen, until the Aswan Dam put a stop to it in the 1950s.

Irrigation is immensely valuable. One third of cultivated land is irrigated, and that land provides two-thirds of the world's food. But irrigation carries many dangers: from soil pollution to the creation of deserts in the places whence the water is drawn. If it is overdone, then the bonanza quickly gives way to desert. Huge tracts of western and southern Australia have already been lost to salt, dragged up from below. The logic of the present global market says

'So what?' In the short term there are fortunes to be made, and the future can take care of itself. Technology can always find a way, we are told. But it doesn't always, and this is no way to run a world.

Even more broadly: very high yields are commonly achieved not simply by new and fancy crops, not simply by irrigation, but by huge inputs of industrial chemicals: fertiliser (including N), pesticides, fungicides, herbicides. In 'conventional', meaning industrialised systems, the soil itself is generally taken for granted, with no specific attempt to retain its texture or volume. (In absolute contrast, in organic systems—at least as conceived by Lady Eve Balfour, who founded Britain's Soil Association the soil is given priority). Very forgiving, deep soils, with a perfect balance of clay (holds water), sand (drainage) and organic material (texture, fertility) in temperate climates (tropical soils don't readily retain organic material) can withstand the rigours of intensive exploitation for decade after decade. Some even improve over time. After all, heavily fertilised soils of particularly favourable structure and in sympathetic, temperate climates can increase their organic content year by year because a large proportion of the total biomass of any crop grows underground in the form of roots which remain after harvesting. But most tropical soils, and many temperate soils, are soon eroded by such bullish treatment. So it is that the wonderfully fertile soils of Britain's East Anglia, our cereal belt, have sunk by several metres since Mediaeval times. They are easy to plough because they are rich in peat, the pickled remains of ancient moss; and as the soil is turned the peat is exposed and oxidises away. The cereal fields of East Anglia must be actively drained, by pumping. But the pumping becomes harder as the soil shrinks and dries and blows away and soon we will be down to bedrock clay, and the fields will not be worth draining at all. Then the area will flood; and, because of global warming and rising sea-levels, the flooding will be quicker and more extensive.

The powers-that-be of confident (though now rather anxious), trading Britain, clearly feel that it is acceptable to write off our principal source of home-grown wheat and barley. The same kind of scenario—different in detail but similar in principle—is being repeated a thousand or a million times worldwide. The rapid conversion of the Amazon rainforest first into poor grazing and then into desert, is the best-known example—but the devastation of the Cerrado, Brazil's dry forest, is even more dramatic. The gratuitous ploughing of Greek hillside and English downland is smaller in scale but equally horrible in its way. Overall, the destruction is a serious blow to the world as a whole and to all humanity. It results entirely from the desire to maximise yields in the short term, without regard for the long term. Without regard for our children, that is.

Clearly, the erosion of East Anglia, and eroded hillsides worldwide began long before the global market came on line. Even Homer complained of soil erosion, some centuries before Plato. Clearly, though, the current zeal for maximisation of yield, made possible in the short term by heavy engineering and high tech, and urged on ever more shrilly by the desire and assumed desirability of maximising turnover in order to maximise wealth, will make things a great deal worse, far more rapidly than was ever possible in the past. One of the most horrible aspects of the whole sorry scene is that we *could* be using our present science and engineering truly to create a safe world that is good for everyone. Instead, we are deploying science and the high technologies it gives rise to primarily and often exclusively for short-term profit. The fabulous insights that science provides us with, which could and should be among our greatest assets, instead are boosting a world economy and order that are threatening to kill us all off. It is as if the aim was to bring on the apocalypse. It is beyond belief. But it is the way things are.

What's wrong with adding value?

Adding value is good—if value is truly added, and is not otherwise harmful. I will pay a good price for a good loaf. Good bakers add value, and are among the world's most valuable citizenry (though of course, in this modern age, they have largely been replaced by vastly inferior high-tech mass production). I will pay a small fortune for excellent sausages, lovingly fashioned by people who know what they are doing. Good bakers and sausage-makers truly add value. They deserve our thanks. In a world that took serious things seriously, they would be the ones we honoured.

But value-adding in our modern, debased, simplified economy is something quite different. The core idea is not to add worth, but to increase expense: to increase the money that can be charged. Much of what is done is obviously spurious: excess packaging; French beans jetted with subsidised fuel from Kenyan hillsides to suburban supermarkets (only people who can't cook would dream of serving Kenyan French beans); bright red strawberries whisked for no worthwhile reason at all between continents, to be served out of season, as if their chilly wateriness was somehow life-enhancing. It is all so obviously fatuous I will not waste words on it.

What does require comment, and is usually overlooked, is that the entire modern livestock industry has almost nothing to do with good agriculture, or with good nutrition or gastronomy, but is entirely an exercise in value-adding. Again the industry is designed primarily to make the people who control it (usually not the farmers) enormously rich, and in this it succeeds spectacularly. But is horribly cruel to animals and people alike, creates horrendous pollution, and in general is a huge threat to the security of the Earth as a whole and hence to all humanity.

The nonsense of modern livestock

As outlined in chapter 3, livestock can enhance the biological efficiency of agriculture, and improve our nutritional status and gastronomic delectation but only if the animals are produced in ways that reflect their own biology and the physical restraints of landscape. Committed herbivores such as cattle and sheep should primarily be fed on grass or browse, which is to say on leaves, which in biochemical terms means cellulose, which human beings cannot eat, and which are grown in places where it is hard to grow cereals. The omnivores, mainly pigs and poultry, should be fed as was traditional on leftovers and substandard or surplus crops. Both the herbivores and the omnivores may be given some grain to help them through the winter (so that there are more of them in spring, to make better use of the summer grazing) and to help cows through their lactation. But grain is given very much as a supplement.

However, farmers in principle face one huge economic hurdle which they have often found hard to overcome. The title of my earlier book was too true. Feeding people can be too easy. If people ate as recommended in chapter 3 and as most of humanity has done through most of history and prehistory—plenty of plants, not much meat, and maximum variety—then we could well be fed on a fairly modest output. But this would mean that the market for food would be 'inelastic'. The demand could soon be met. As societies grow richer, makers of cars can grow richer in parallel, because however wealthy people may become they can always spend more on cars—one for each day of the week; an SUV and a run-about; a Lamborghini and a couple of Ferraris for fun; and so on. But if those same people are content simply to eat good food (plenty of plants, not much meat, and maximum variety) then the farmers miss out. Adult humans generally need about 1500 kcals per day just to stay alive. But even the richest cannot get through much more than about 3000, unless they take up rowing, or spend their evenings in the gym, or are prepared to grow fat. Where's the profit in that?

Meat solves the problem. If wheat is turned into bread, leavened or unleavened (as in chapattis and parathas and goodness knows what), which is the sensible thing to do, then we can all eat well for pennies (if we have good bakers). But far more cash can be generated overall if that same wheat is first fed to pigs and poultry—or indeed, in these extraordinary days when sound biology has been put on hold, to cattle. So it is, just to repeat the point, that half the wheat now grown in the world is fed to livestock, 80 per cent of the maize, and well over 90 per cent of the soya. The excess meat thus produced is mostly consumed in the west, where the main health problem is obesity and its related ills, brought about largely by too much animal fat, but what the hell. The extra production has nothing at all to do with sound nutrition or with fine gastronomy, because the cooking that goes with all this surplus livestock—the 99p burger and wall-to-wall fried chicken—is unspeakable even though, alas, it is all that many people have access to. Livestock fed on grain that we could eat ourselves does not enhance overall efficiency. Such livestock competes with us. By 2050, if livestock production continues to increase at its present rate, then the world's farm animals will be consuming the equivalent of four billion people—equal to the total world population in the 1970s, when many feared there were too many to feed. So by 2050 livestock will be increasing the effective population that needs to be fed by 50 per cent: nine billion people, plus four billion animals. If present economic principles continue, then we can be fairly sure that if poor people in Third World countries are competing for food with western cattle, then the cattle will win. Just as they do now. We can pay more for cereal for cattle-feed than poor people can pay to feed their children. That's the market.

But livestock fed on cereal and soya solves the farmers' most fundamental economic problem. It removes the theoretical ceiling on production and hence on wealth. Ten tonnes of wheat would solve the nutritional problems of about 30 people for a year—if they ate a traditional diet. But if the same wheat is first fed to livestock, then the resultant meat would feed only about five people. So cereal production can be increased. To be sure, the meat market can be saturated too, so although the ceiling on production is raised by feeding cereal en masse to livestock, it does not seem at first sight as if the market has been made truly elastic. But there is an easy way around this. Traditional cuisines make use of *all* parts of the animal: tripes, kidneys, feet: bring 'em on. But although I have bought tripe in Spanish supermarkets, I have never seen it in an English supermarket. We British are already too rich for that. In practice, the livestock market can be expanded indefinitely because when there are enough animals to feed everybody, the traders can simply throw most of each animal away—all but the most expensive cuts, the chops and steaks. Then if you ask for tripe or kidneys they can proffer their standard mendacious excuse: 'We don't stock them because there is no demand'. Since, to an ever-increasing extent, thanks to the idleness and pusillanimity of modern, corporate-controlled governments, the supermarkets now control the flow of information as well as the food supply itself, they can ensure that the cheap cuts that have launched some of the world's finest recipes are written out of the act. A whole generation has grown up that does not know of their existence (and if told of it, pulls a face. Children are being brought up to prefer additive-rich reconstituted chicken shaped into dinosaurs. Value-adding writ large).

In short, the production of livestock by modern means—turning cheap cereal and pulses into expensive meat—is the most flagrant and widespread exercise in value adding of all. It is, indeed, extremely lucrative. It also ensures that humanity's chances of surviving in a tolerable world are hugely reduced. For good, modern industrial livestock production is extraordinarily cruel to livestock and producers alike, and of course is helping to eliminate our fellow species (by increasing the demands that humanity as a whole makes upon the Earth).

But the third requirement of standard business practice—cut costs to the bone, and then cut them again—is the most pernicious of all.

Cutting costs

Nothing has harmed our world and the people in it more than the frenetic desire, and the perceived need, to farm on the cheap.

For one thing, cut-price agriculture is extremely dangerous. To begin with, again as outlined in chapter 3, cheap farming is simplified farming—the biggest possible fields with the biggest possible machines to achieve economy of scale; single kinds of crops grown horizon to horizon—large-scale monoculture—so that all can be harvested together, with one sweep of the combine. Hedges, copses, and islands of higher ground among the paddy fields for horticulture, are swept aside. Biodiversity is lost and so too is the essential nutritional variety. In addition, because the vast crops are uniform, all are vulnerable to the same diseases. One particularly virulent strain of one pathogen could wipe out the whole lot.

It is particularly dangerous—and cruel—to produce livestock on the cheap. Britain's recent epidemic of bovine spongiform encephalopathy, BSE, was caused entirely by the perceived need to cut costs. BSE is a horrible disease that attacks the nervous system, first causing the animal to stagger, and quickly and virtually invariably leading to death. It is caused by a prion, the same class of agent (not really an organism; just a deformed protein) that causes scrapie in sheep and kuru in human beings. It is spread when animals directly consume tissue, particularly nervous tissue, of other animals. Normally prions spread only between animals of the same species. Kuru seems to be confined to people who have practiced cannibalism.

Until BSE turned up, cattle were not known to be susceptible to prion diseases. They do not generally eat flesh of any kind, and certainly not that of other cattle (though they may be exposed to placentae if they all give birth together, so there may be some flesh-to-flesh transmission). But dairy cattle are traditionally given extra feed, including extra protein—so-called 'concentrate'—during lactation. Now that yields must be maximised, to maximise profit, they are given more and more concentrate. Cereals are the traditional protein source. Soya is now the leader, which is why Amazonia and the Cerrado are being blitzed. But it can be cheapest of all to make protein concentrate from bits of dead animals, including dead cows. Whatever is cheapest must, of course be done. So in recent decades, cows have been turned into cannibals. Not nice; but that's modern business.

All went well (apart from the disgustingness of it) until the 1980s when restrictions were lifted on the method of preparation, to save fuel, and hence bring the cost down even more. Then it was found that cattle flesh can contain rogue prions (which may or may not have been acquired from sheep). They spread like wildfire. They also spread to humans who had eaten cattle flesh—in the form of vCJD (variant Creutzfeld-Jacob) disease, related to kuru. Variant CJD kills people just as surely and horribly as BSE kills cattle. A lot of people eat beef, and professor Roy Anderson, a leading British epidemiologist, at one point estimated that as many as 100,000 people might be infected with the prion, and almost all of them, from what we know of the disease, would die. His worst prognostications have not come about but the game is not over yet—CJD can have a very long incubation period—and several have died already.

Traditional farmers know that the prime rule of good animal husbandry is to interrupt chains of infection, and preferably to avoid them all together. But in the case of BSE, a chain of infection was actively created where none had ever existed before—for cows in a state of nature do not eat other cows. Brilliant, eh? But that's business. Nobody was blamed for this fiasco, of course, although a few civil servants, who of course were not named and in any case were not in any worthwhile sense guilty, were rapped over the knuckles in an extremely expensive official report that was not, of course, briefed to look at the overall farming strategy. Whatever way you look at it, the BSE-vCJD episode has been a disgrace: thoroughly bad practice that should have been condemned on grounds of common sense and common decency, elevated to official policy; and then covered up. But that's modern business—and modern government.

Britain's other great gift to modern agriculture came in 2001: the biggest epidemic in history of foot and mouth disease (FMD). FMD is caused by a virus. It affects all animals with cloven hooves such as cattle, sheep, goats, and pigs. It is highly contagious and spreads by various means, both through direct contact and through the air. It does not normally kill a healthy animal but it is unpleasant and seriously debilitating and if left to run its course may reduce the subsequent performance of the animal throughout its life: for example depressing milk yield.

FMD can be controlled by vaccination, though not absolutely: vaccination may merely mask latent infection. So it is reasonable at least in an island like Britain to keep it at bay simply by ensuring that the virus never gets into the country at all. This is how we controlled rabies through most of the 20th century, and with great success. But Britain took rabies seriously. Rabies affects pets and people. FMD merely affects farm animals. So whereas it was extremely difficult to smuggle a dog into Britain through most of the 20th century (and smuggling carried huge penalties) it was a breeze to bring in raw meat, which could be infected. Journalists demonstrated this for a stunt as the FMD epidemic ran its course.

So it seems that FMD was brought in to Britain some time before 2001—although for all anyone knows the virus might have been lingering for years in sub-clinical form in upland sheep. We don't have enough vets these days to check such things (too expensive). But the FMD virus certainly did arrive by one route or another and because Britain's livestock are not vaccinated against it, the virus found very rich pickings. The previous British outbreak of FMD was in late 1967. But although that outbreak was then the world's biggest it remained largely confined to the north-west, around Cheshire, which is a traditional centre of dairy farming. In today's cut-price world local abattoirs have been closed and animals are whisked from one end of the country to the other for the dubious privilege of being killed in an EU approved super-duper slaughter-house. Animals sometimes travelled long distances in traditional systems but traditionally they walked, and the journey took weeks, so any illness that any of them had became apparent en route. Nowadays the longest journeys are completed well within the incubation period even of a virulent virus like FMD.

Sot it was that the first cases in the 2001 outbreak were reported on February 20 from an abattoir in Essex in the south-east of England, but were thought to have come from a farm in Northumberland, nearly 300 miles to the north. Within days it had reached Devon in the south-west and the last reported case, on September 30, was from Cumbria, in the north-west. In effect it was chauffeured, tourist class, to the far corners of the country, and then for good measure spread to Holland and France. By the time it had run its course it had infected animals on 2030 UK farms, all over the country. In the absence of vaccination, control was attempted and eventually achieved by slaughtering infected animals and those around them. Four million were killed, and were burned in huge pyres that featured nightly on the television news (although politicians insisted that they were 'exaggerated'. Apparently the 100-foot-high flames were 'got up by the press'). The overall cost was put at £10 billion, about one per cent of Britain's GDP. Even the Royal Shakespeare

Company was hit because Americans in particular very reasonably decided to give Britain a miss while the epidemic was on.

The FMD virus does not infect human beings—or not so far, anyway. But most human infections began as zoonoses (animal diseases) and we should always be alert to possible mutations, and the horrible death of so many animals is far from trivial. Besides, some people did die. Some farmers committed suicide—even more than has become usual.

Britain's politicians and the industrialists alike exhort us with vehemence worthy of John Wesley to practice obsessive hygiene. Manufacturers of disinfectant are given carte blanche to warn young mums that unless their kitchens gleam like intensive care units their babies will surely succumb to something vile (although they present no evidence for this). Little old ladies who make cakes for the village fête are told not to break the eggs on the side of the mixing bowl, for fear of some shell-borne microbe. The officially appointed Food Standards Agency with great pomp occasionally advises the withdrawal of some additive or other, from among the many hundreds that lace the modern diet. Yet Britain's whole agricultural system is run on a wing and a prayer. If modern livestock production had been designed by a crack team of pathogens, they could scarcely have done the job better.

Yet there is worse. Most destructive by far is that cut-price agriculture puts people out of work. Indeed, in the interests of reducing costs, it is expressly designed to do so. This is discussed in chapter 5: it is so important it requires us, humanity, to re-think the way we are structuring the entire world. To anticipate: if all the world followed the western way of farming, as they are exhorted and often obliged to do, up to two billion people worldwide would be without livelihood; and despite the enthusiasm shown in high places for IT and tourism, and hairdressing and the re-cycling of old tyres, there is nothing useful or sustainable for most of those dispossessed people to do. Unemployment is the royal road to poverty. Politicians and captains of industry assure us that they desire above all to 'make poverty history' and in this they are supported by celebs of all kinds, to add street-cred. But the methods they advocate—more westernisation: high tech and the global market—are guaranteed to create poverty on a scale that even in this miserable world is still hard to conceive. Even in this age of official absurdity the muddle-headedness beggars belief.

In short, although capitalism in some form or other may still offer the world its best options—it really should be possible to reconcile personal freedom with social justice, as the US founders envisaged—the present, simplified, consciously amoral form of it is highly destructive. At least, the ruthless global market may benefit some industries; but it is as antipathetic to the cause of enlightened agriculture—agriculture that is intended actually to feed people—as can be conceived.

Yet even people who can see the horrors and absurdity of the present-day food supply chain are apt to make excuses for it. Doesn't it provide us with cheap food—at least in the west? Wouldn't food be far more expensive if agriculture was run along more enlightened lines? In an age in which routine mendacity is merely a tactic, this is still among the most pernicious of all lies.

The illusion of cheap food

I used to shop when I could at a couple of traditional markets where beans are sold en masse in paper sacks and vegetables come straight out of boxes and it all costs about a third, and sometimes only a tenth, of what the same things would cost in supermarkets. Food is as dear as it is largely because of middle-men's mark-ups. Take away the fripperies, and the cost can come down dramatically.

Nonetheless, at least in the short term, food produced by the methods of Enlightened Agriculture would probably be more expensive than a lot of the food in modern-day supermarkets appears to be. It is impossible at this stage to say how much dearer it would be, for reasons that will become apparent in the following paragraphs. But, for example, a local farmer friend of mine tells me that his free-range chickens, raised under trees (chickens are basically jungle fowl) and fed a natural diet, take twice as long to reach market weight as those raised intensively in sheds, and require much more space, and so they are bound to cost at least three times as much as the 'conventional' industrial kind. So the defenders of the status quo do seem to have a point. But actually, it's not much of one.

For in truth, *there is no such thing as cheap food*. If chickens ever sell in the supermarket for 50p per pound as they often do, or tins of fruit are offered at three for the price of two, then we can be sure that some person or society or animal or landscape, somewhere along the supply chain, is being screwed. Some farmer is working for less than the cost of production; his workers are paid slave-wages; the animals are packed in cages, with the lights dimmed, and a body-full of growth-promoters; some hillside is being eroded, some forest felled, some river polluted—and all the creatures who used to live in those hills and forests and rivers, and all the people who enjoyed them and made their living from them, are being swept aside. Or, as Britain's epidemics of BSE and FMD demonstrated, the farming is being run on a wing and a prayer. Or, as often is the case when supermarkets seem sometimes to give the goods away, some market ploy is afoot, destined to put some local trader out of work. The food is cheap only because, for various reasons, the true costs are not taken into account. Who picks up the bill for the local fishermen when a prawn farm wipes out the mangroves, where the fish breed? Who cares? But somebody, somewhere, is suffering; and sooner or later, all of us will be picking up the bill.

Overall, too, supermarket food is not intended to be cheap. Individual items may be cheap, to be sure, but a key component of the market economy is to 'add value'; which means, to make dear. Traditional cooking based primarily on fresh, local ingredients should in principle be able to supply far better nutrition and gastronomy more cheaply. If it currently fails to do so it is because the present economy is rigged in favour of mass production and mass long-distance transport. Food from traditional markets is not gratuitously packaged and processed. Traditional people do their own cooking. Even more to the point, traditional cooking exemplifies the general rule both of sound nutrition and of excellent cuisine: plenty of plants, not much meat, and maximum variety. The industrialised suppliers, by contrast, strive to push us ever further up the food chain—since meat is innately more profitable than staples. You can still eat wonderfully for pennies in villages in Turkey not simply because of the exchange rate but because the food is variations on a theme of wheat and honey and herbs, raised locally, and cooked in the back of the shop by people who know what they are doing and do not need to waste money on marketing and neon signs. One of Britain's biggest supermarket chains recently sold full-sized (what used to be called 'two-pound') loaves for 20p. Their television ads in effect acknowledged that the bread was rubbish. It was best toasted, they said (although lousy bread makes lousy toast). Yet in truth there is nothing dearer than a 20p loaf. If bread is good, you can eat a great deal of it. When France was at its culinary height the French ate bread at every meal, and often with very little else; just a touch of cheese and sausage and the occasional leek. But what bread! I remember how magnificent it was. Such bread can still be found, here and there. The memory of it is not an illusion. If bread makes up half your diet, then it is cheap at £2.00 a loaf. Uneatable bread merely provides wrapping for whatever is considered more esculent but relatively speaking will be extremely expensive (like industrial chicken in industrial mayonnaise with a token frond of damp lettuce. As Snoopy was wont to say: 'Eeaagh!').

But let us shift the argument. *Why* should food be cheap? Again, half a century ago when their food was still great, French people on average spent 30 per cent of their income on food. Why not? They built their lives around it—and very civilised they were too. You didn't have to be middle class, and certainly not a poseur, to be a gourmet. Some of the finest cafés of all time were designed for French lorry drivers. Even now on the continent of Europe—France, Italy, Spain, Greece, even Germany—you see entire extended families gathered around vast restaurant tables in the evening, with the children falling asleep in situ ('It takes a village to bring up a child', as they say in Africa); not rich families, but ordinary working people. What is better? What else is life for, if not for such sociality? The British currently spend an estimated 14 per cent of their income on food—and still 'demand' that it should be cheaper. Why? Perhaps because so much of it is rubbish, and the less you spend on it, the better. If it was good, perhaps we would see the point of spending quite a bit more.

Finally, though, we should question the sanctimonious argument that food must be cheap for the sake of the poor. In countries that have always been poor, food has often become far dearer in recent years because home-grown food has largely given way to commodity crops, sold for cash that stays in the hands of the entrepreneurs. In countries like Britain and the US, both fabulously rich by world standards, we should ask, 'Why do they have poor people at all?' There are many reasons for poverty of course but the general answer, in both countries, is injustice. Many people in these rich countries remain poor because the economy is designed above all to ensure that some people are extremely rich. The economy is designed to be maximally competitive (although if you are rich enough you can cheat) but it is not designed to be equitable. The antidote to poverty is to give a damn, and create economies with fairer shares. The answer is not to be cruel to animals, or to screw farmers into the ground, or to fell forests and pollute rivers. These are the methods of the scoundrel.

In short, the globalized market does not serve us well. It may work well for motor-cars and white goods but agriculture is different, and it is demonstrably bad for agriculture. Farmers are in the front-line, and they are suffering already. China, India, South Korea and others are apparently doing well out of the global market because they are making the things that the market is good for. But all their farmers are suffering—in South Korea the suicide rate has become horrendous—and as globalisation bites they will suffer more; and farmers and their families, worldwide, account for about four-tenths of all humanity. Soon we will all suffer—and indeed are already suffering—because agriculture that really works and is sustainable needs good farmers, and plenty of them. It needs to be labour intensive. All of us need it to be labour intensive. The economic system that is making it impossible to be labour intensive is killing all of us.

So what can we do about it?

Can we do better?

The short answer, I believe, is yes. Various think-tanks and individuals around the world are on the case, taking their lead both from ecologists and from professional economists. Many practical schemes are already up and running. These include cooperatives of many kinds; trusts; clubs; social franchise; micro-credit; local currencies. If these initiatives and models can be built upon, and if they can be coordinated, then already, perhaps, we have the basis of what the world needs. We are intending to explore the various options in depth in the College for Enlightened Agriculture—of which more later.

In short, the task before us is not to confront big governments and the corporates, for that is merely exhausting. We need instead to create viable and clearly superior alternatives, and allow the status quo to wither on the vine. To do this, we need only to build on what exists already. In the final chapter I discuss how we might bring the necessary change about within the specific and crucial context of food. In the next and penultimate chapter I want to broaden the discussion and ask what a society would look like if it really did have an economy geared to its own wellbeing, and really was concerned for its own children and for the world as a whole. Such a society would, in fact, be agrarian.

CHAPTER 5

Renaissance: the New Agrarianism

If we don't solve the world's food problems, and soon, we'll have had our chips. If we continue to farm as destructively as we now do, then everything has had its chips. We are sawing away the branch on which we all sit—our own species, and the several million others with whom we share this Earth. Some of course will survive, but we cannot say which. If we change the climate more than a little, as we are on course to do, then the whole world becomes a lottery. We can at least be reasonably certain that all the big land animals will die out, because they are particularly vulnerable for all kinds of reasons. All we can say about the rest is that nature is full of surprises, and cannot be second-guessed. There's no way of knowing what will happen, but we can be sure that in the short term at least (the next few thousand or million years) it will not be for the better.

If we are to solve our problems then, even at this late hour, we need to re-think everything from first principles. A lot of the necessary thinking has already been done—certainly enough to be going on with; enough to get us out of the present hole if only it was applied. The real problem lies with the powers-that-be (an expression first coined by St Paul, albeit in a somewhat different context). The world is still ruled by corporates and banks, in alliance with governments including the kind that are elected, like those of Britain and the US, who have not grasped the nature of the problem and are hell-bent on strategies and policies that are likely to kill us all.

Worst of all, is that the powers-that-be have convinced themselves, and seem to have convinced a lot of people at large including a lot of unthinking journalists, that they are doing the right thing. Neoliberalism applied to agriculture threatens to kill us all for the reasons we have seen but is nonetheless taken as a 'given'. Politicians queue up on television to assure us that they 'believe in the market'—meaning that they apparently believe in the status quo: a 'free' market which in reality is controlled by a few big players. Politicians, economists, and scientists of a certain kind (not the kind that know about farming) queue up to assure us that without high-tech, of which GMOs are taken as the prime example, we are bound to starve. Their ignorance seems absolute, yet is sublime. Despite this they also affect to occupy the moral high ground. Since they acknowledge no alternative to neoliberalism (for Margaret Thatcher famously assured us 20 years ago that there is no alternative) or to GMOs and comparable high technologies, they insist that all protestors are Luddite (in the bad sense), elitist, woolly-minded, head-in-the-clouds 'romantics', or new-agers seeking to re-create a world that never was. The high-tech neoliberals may sometimes appear to behave harshly but, they assure us, they alone know what's good for us. The apparent failures of the present time are caused largely by our own recalcitrance—the failure of humanity at large, known as 'the public', to embrace high tech and neoliberal market economics as enthusiastically as they deserve. Our rulers are like those physicians parodied in many a Victorian novel who kill their patients with their physic, but continue in the face of all the evidence and of common sense to ply them with more and more; a little more mercury, a little more bleeding, a little more heat, will surely bring about a cure.

So for those of us who give a damn, and who are not convinced that more of the same will cure the world's obvious ills, there are two outstanding tasks. The first is to re-think agriculture and all that goes with it (which in truth is all of life) from first principles. The second is to apply the new ways of thinking *despite* the powers-that-be, who are very powerful indeed and who (God save us) include our elected governments. Both are huge tasks and we are likely to fail. But we have to give it our best shot because the price of failure is absolute. Above all, we should surely bear in mind the title of this book—that we can supply Good Food for Everyone Forever. *Feeding People is Easy*—the title of this book's precursor—is only a little hyperbolic. It *ought* to be. It's only bad ideas espoused by powerful people and driven by all-but uncontrollable institutions and fiscal mechanisms that are getting in the way. It is the case, though, that if we really want the world to be a better place—if we want our children and grandchildren to live tolerable lives, and other people's children and grandchildren, and our fellow species—then we have to do the job ourselves, *despite* the powerful institutions, which include our own elected governments. Hence the subtitle of this book: *A people's takeover of the world's food supply.*

So let us look first at the basic principles that we need to re-address and get right; and then look at the means by which we, people at large who give a damn, Ordinary Joes, can make good things happen.

The big ideas re-addressed

In truth we need re-thinking across the board. As follows:

The economy

It isn't enough to fiddle with the status quo, in the way that modern politicians and economists fiddle. A bit on tax here and a bit off tax there can make a difference, but it does not get to the roots of things. Neither, on the other hand, should we plunge again into the traditional cold-war battle between the centralized, 'Marxist' economy of communism, and the somewhat ill-defined spectrum of de-centralized economies broadly classed as capitalism. Instead, I suggest two ways forward.

First, and most fundamentally, we need to re-define what the economy actually *is*. Nowadays it is conceived primarily or indeed entirely as an exercise in making and sorting money. I have often been in the company of economists-qua-accountants who say things like 'At the end of the day, what counts in the bottom line'—meaning that all that matters in the end is the total amount of cash that's left when you tot up all the pluses and minuses. In recent years John Elkington, who specializes in 'sustainable development', pointed out that money isn't all that matters. At least equally important are the state of the environment in general, and the lives of people—happiness, justice, freedom. So he suggested 'the triple bottom line': economic, environmental, and social.

Beyond doubt, the 'triple bottom line' is an advance over crude arithmetic but I don't feel it goes far enough. The fundamental mistake is to give the economy—equated with money—equal status with the world at large (the 'environment') and with the state of society. The economy is *not* fundamental. It is a means to an end. The real fundamentals are twofold. The first has to do with physical and biological reality: how the world really works; what it is capable of; what we and our fellow creatures need in order to survive. The second has to do with morality. What is it *right* to do. How ought we to behave?

The first of these considerations—what is possible and what is necessary—are, I suggest, matters of biology. The second—what is it right to do?—are matters of moral philosophy and also (many might say) of aesthetics, both of which are underpinned by metaphysics (which commonly manifests in the context of religion, and asks the most fundamental questions of all—what is the world *really* like, beneath what science can tell us?). But let's keep it simple and say that the fundamental issues are biological—which are matters of physical reality; and moral—what it is right to do.

The economy, then, emerges not as an end itself, which is how it is now treated; or as one player among three, as in the model of the triple bottom line; but simply as a *device*. It becomes the medium, the matrix, the mechanism that enables people to do the things they think are right, within the context of what is possible. In the end, it is hard and perhaps impossible to remove the subjective element from moral thinking. We just have to go with our gut feelings. It's often pointed out that different people feel differently and so, the argument goes, 'morality' is just a personal thing, or a 'relative' thing, that differs from place to place and time to time. There is some truth in this—but not much. For common observation and a great deal of theory show us that most people who we consider to be sane certainly do agree on the broad principles. Most who are not obviously psychopathic agree that kindness is better than cruelty; that it is better to try to feed people than to let them starve; that it is better to try to conserve our fellow creatures than to wipe them out. Common sense, then, and common humanity, tell us that these broad principles can surely be taken as moral imperatives. In short, the moral principles emerge from our own consciences—not quite universally, but near enough; and the basics—kindness, generosity, justice, humility—have been reinforced this past few thousand years (and doubtless before) by all the formal and traditional religions that I know about.

To some extent, the physical realities of the Earth within which we all have to live are obvious enough. It doesn't need formal science to tell us that too much farming can lead to soil erosion. Homer pointed this out 800 years before Christ (and farmers had doubtless known this for thousands of years before Homer). But it does take science to tell us, as it is telling us, that too much CO_2 in the atmosphere can throw the world into ecological tailspin, or that organochlorine pesticide residues and industrial oestrogen mimics get everywhere—and so on and so on. So we can in broad terms easily agree on the physical and moral guidelines, that should determine the nature of an economy that truly served the needs of humanity and of the world at large. So what, in practice, would such an economy look like?

I suggest it would be nothing more nor less than a kind of old-fashioned capitalism. This was, and still is, common-sense commerce and trade, with a strong moral input: a genuine desire to do good rather than harm; a prevailing honesty; common sense. This is the kind of commerce that turned Britain into a nation of small shopkeepers, as Napoleon (disparagingly) put the matter, and the US into a nation of small farmers, as Jefferson said (approvingly). Such simple capitalism albeit with a few refinements could again serve the world's interests very well. I have met many a traditional businessperson who agrees with this absolutely—indeed the idea was first put into my head by a former director of a major oil company who, he says, hates the turn that capitalism has taken. The kind of economy that could serve the world well, in short, really isn't very frightening. There are no reds under the bed. What really is frightening—terrifying, in fact—is the status quo: the huge corporate machines that are controlled by no individuals and exist solely to maximize (and concentrate) wealth; and the mega-banks that control the world not by engaging with its realities but by an abstract game played with hypothetical finance.

Governance

We, humanity, especially in the western world, have allowed ourselves to be horribly conned. We have allowed ourselves to be persuaded that we, human beings, are a fundamentally bad lot. St Augustine of Hippo in the 5th century AD got Christianity off onto a pessimistic and oppressive foot by emphasizing the concept of original sin. Adam had defied God, and his descendants—all of us—are all born guilty, and must spend our lives making up for it. The Ancient Greeks, the Romans, and the European rationalists of the 18th century reached much the same conclusion by a different route: that the hoi polloi, the plebs, the mob, which is most of us, were and are a thoroughly bad lot. Only strong government could stop us from tearing each other to pieces.

Thomas Robert Malthus (known cozily as 'Bob' to his friends and family), from the end of the 18th century onwards, made matters worse by suggesting that there were simply too many of us. The mob bred like rabbits. Darwin, liberal and civilized gentleman though he was, made the whole notion scientifically respectable by suggesting that all evolutionary change in nature was brought about by competition. Darwin himself eschewed the notion of progress in evolution, but many of his successors took it to be self-evident that evolution does lead to progress, and so concluded that progress of any kind is impossible without competition. In recent decades Richard Dawkins coined the expression 'selfish gene' and although he has insisted ever since that selfish genes do not necessarily produce selfish individuals, a superficial reading suggests that all creatures including human beings are 'naturally' selfish because we are driven by selfish genes, which are in head-to-head competition with each other. In practice, what people understand by ideas is more important than what their authors intend them to mean. Now we have an economy that is competitive to its roots (apart from the special interests of the big players and the cartels of course) and encourages selfishness; and it perceives the ruthlessness and the selfishness to be natural, and therefore 'right'.

In reality, the idea that what is natural is *ipso facto* right is crude in the extreme; and so too is the idea that human beings and other creatures *are* 'naturally' selfish. In truth, Augustine's original sin was little more than a piece of personal theologizing, simply his own opinion. The Greek and Roman patricians and intellectuals said what it was convenient to them to believe, since it gave them an excuse for ruling. So too did those of the European Enlightenment. 'Twas ever thus. Malthus and Darwin were children of their times—very grim times indeed!—and this coloured their views even further.

In truth, a modern, cool assessment of biology leads us to conclude that the best survival tactic is not all-out competition. Co-operation is far more fruitful. Life as a whole is innately cooperative. If it were not, living cells, and organisms, and societies, and ecosystems, would fall apart. Sound Darwinian thinking could lead us to conclude that the fight should go not to the selfish and the ultra-competitive, but to the generous and co-operative. Common observation of people worldwide, when they are not stressed, surely leads us to conclude that most of us, most of the time, left to ourselves, behave very well indeed; that morality is built into us.

All this has tremendous implications for all of politics. For the Patricians of Greece and Rome, and the politicians and ruling priests the world over, have justified their dominance on moral grounds: that without their civilizing influence, we would be killing each other. True democracy would be dangerous because it would mean 'mob rule' and that would obviously be a disaster. So the best we do by way of democracy is to allow ourselves to vote, every now and again, for some *de facto* patrician—who then very kindly looks after us, in return for honours, riches, and a fat pension. In truth it's a protection racket.

What a con. Given that most people are nice rather than nasty, a society that truly reflected human instincts—which would be a true democracy—should be rather pleasant. It would surely be more co-operative than competitive—like, say, the traditional peasant-based agriculture of Poland. In reality, most wars and pogroms and all the rest have been caused by rulers, and commonly by self-righteous rulers, with 'right' on their side. Historical analysis has shown that there has never been a significant war between any two 'true' de-mocracies (although the criteria by which true democracy is defined are somewhat low). On the specific matter of agriculture the Nobel prize-winning economist Amartya Sen has pointed out that there has never been a famine in a true democracy.

In short, the thing we really need to do, worldwide, is to make democracy work; and to acknowledge that the version of it we have now, even in the countries that are proudest of their democratic inheritance, are a very poor imitation of what it ought to mean. Specifically, the democracies of Britain and the United States are entirely beholden to the neoliberal economy, based on the idea that competition is all, and that this is right because it is natural. There never have been such stupid or more damaging ideas. But they are what keeps the ruling class (and there really is such a thing) in the position it likes to occupy.

It will be hard to change the economy because the powers-that-be are well-entrenched; and perhaps even harder to install true democ-racy. Yet even such changes, although necessary, are not sufficient. Above all, we need to gear everything that we do to physical and to biological reality, to ensure that what we attempt to do is not only right, but is also possible and necessary. We need to write the ideas of biology—and particularly of physiology and ecology—into our worldview. We need, in short, to enter 'the age of biology'.

The Age of Biology

We need consciously and deliberately to enter 'The Age of Biology'. That is, we need formally to acknowledge what has been obvious to many people for thousands of years, and probably for many tens of thousands of years: that we are surrounded by literally millions of kinds of other creatures, and that in a host of different ways we are dependent on them, and the world in which we all live marches to its own drum and is fragile. As the matter is often expressed, we are not above nature, we are part of nature, and must act accordingly. Other creatures are our fellow creatures and it is appropriate to regard them as friends and family. We do not imagine that our friends and family exist only for our own convenience and should not by the same token treat other creatures as our playthings, or as litter to be swept out of the way; and should not regard the fabric of the world itself simply as a resource, to be treated as commodities and turned with all speed into money.

The word 'should' of course has moral connotations—that the world is not ours to bully at will. But it also means we would be well advised not to take liberties. We do indeed depend on all our fellow creatures—in ways we have hardly begun to understand. Every schoolchild is told how dependent we are on plants: that they are at the base of all food chains (at least, broadly speaking) and that they and other photosynthetic organisms, including diatoms and cyanobacteria, provide all the oxygen gas in the atmosphere. But the complexity of interrelationships between organisms of all kinds, and between all Earthly life and the climate, and the amount and purity of the water and its distribution, and indeed the nature of the rocks and the landscape as a whole, are only now beginning to become apparent.

Ecologists of course have done much to uncover the subtleties over the past 100 years but in recent decades the British physicist (not a biologist at all), James Lovelock, raised awareness to a new level with his Gaia hypothesis—in which he suggested that we should consider the entire ecosystem of the entire Earth as one great organism. One of the best summaries of the whole idea is in

Stephan Harding's *The Animate Earth* (Green Books, Devon, 2006). Children's books like to list creatures that are useful to us in one way or another—all the plants that provide us with food, fibres, dyes, timber, and so on and so on; and all the creatures that we have domesticated and many that largely remain wild, but we rely on nonetheless—such as bumblebees (which pollinate clover which maintains the fertility of the soil). In other popular books and on the scarier kinds of natural films on television we are confronted with nasties which, we are told, we should get rid of. But the more you look at wild nature through the eyes of an ecologist the more you see the extent to which everything depends on everything else, and the creatures we might crudely conceive to be our 'enemies' are often our friends, once you trace the relationships through. What counts overall is stability—which requires resilience: the ability to remain functional, however the conditions may change. Intuition tells us that stability depends very largely on diversity and although some research has sometimes suggested that this is not true, overall, overwhelmingly, the science supports the intuition. Diversity is the thing.

In all our dealings with nature, however, humility is essential— and many a modern scientist, alas, has lost sight of this. The scientists who seem least humble are the ones who work for governments and for corporates—for governments and corporates succeed by being gung-ho and employ only those people who reinforce their own zeal. There is not much room in the top echelons of power and wealth for people who express doubts, and urge caution.

Humility is essential in science for two reasons. Firstly, science does *not*, as is commonly supposed, and as is commonly implied, deal in unequivocal, once-for-all truths. Certainly it does not offer truth of the kind that lawyers demand in courts of law: the truth, the whole truth, and nothing but the truth. The account it offers us of the world is always partial, always provisional, and always uncertain. To suppose otherwise is not only dangerous, but plain bad philosophy.

How come? Surely the methods of science are sure-fire? It bases its ideas on rock-solid observations that are repeated time and again, does it not? The observations are supported by measurement—again repeated and repeated, with a variety of instruments, to the point where they cannot conceivably be wrong. Once we have measurements we have numbers, and we can play with numbers with a myriad forms of mathematics; and maths, inexorably logical, and again repeated this way and that, cannot be wrong. So we can build a mathematical picture of reality, and from that we can frame hypotheses about the mechanisms; and then we can test those hypotheses by making predictions about the way the world ought to work; and then see if those predictions are right. In other words, we can do experiments. With a thousand specialists on the case, working for decade after decade, there is no scope for error.

So it may seem. But still there are at least four outstanding caveats, and quite a few others besides. First as the Austrian-American genius Kurt Gödel pointed out in 1930, maths isn't all it is cracked up to be. In a nutshell, mathematics will always be incomplete and inconsistencies will always be lurking within mathematics. Maths holds itself up by its own shoe-laces. Secondly, as the Austrian-British philosopher Sir Karl Popper pointed out from the 1930s onwards, scientific hypotheses cannot absolutely be *proved*. They can be disproved—shown beyond doubt to be wrong. But they cannot be shown beyond all doubt to be right. Thirdly, as John Stuart Mill pointed out in the mid-19th century, no matter how much we think we know there could always be things going on that we never thought of at all, and those things could be important. History has shown time and again that it is perfectly possible to tell very coherent stories that seem to explain everything there is to know about the world—and then make some new discovery which shows that some essential ingredient has been left out, and the whole story needs to be re-told from scratch. In short, the accounts of science are always uncertain, always partial, and even if they turned out to be the truth, the whole truth, and nothing but the truth, we could not know that this is the case, because we have no way of knowing what else might be going on that we haven't thought of yet. Finally, as the great 20th century zoologist Sir Peter Medawar put the matter, 'science is the art of the soluble'. In other words, scientists achieve the success they do by making sure that they ask only those questions they think they have a fair chance of answering (in the time and with the resources available). They provide clear answers because they take such care to tailor the questions. All of science, therefore, is a tautology.

All this applies to all science in general. In truth is does not weaken the value of science—its insights are wonderful, and we surely could not be without it at this stage of the game—but the caveats do put it somewhat in perspective.

The reservations multiply a hundred times over when we start to apply the ideas of science to living systems—whether the system in question is the genome (the sum of all the genes), the cell, the organism, the society, the ecosystem, or 'Gaia' as a whole. At any one level of complexity, thousands of factors are relevant which all interact (where 'thousands' is an arbitrary number that in truth stretches away into infinity). We cannot know all of them, or take them all into account. Furthermore, as the particle physicists started to show almost 100 years ago, at the level of the fundamental particles of which all matter is composed, there is a great deal of randomness.

Put the in-built randomness together with the unfathomable complexity and we see that the relationships within wild nature are innately, and deeply, uncertain. Simple Newtonian cause-and-effect, in which object A strikes object B and both move off with a velocity that is perfectly predictable, do not apply. As the physicists like to say, cause and effect in the real world is 'non-linear'; meaning that any one 'cause' can have a virtual infinity of effects and any particular outcome, is guessable at all, is only a matter of probability.

Biologists are sometimes said to suffer from 'physics envy', meaning that they would like their subject to be as precise as that of the physicist. But the most important lesson from physics is that of non-linearity—and that, they often seem reluctant to embrace. In similar vein, applied biologists seem to suffer from engineering envy. Thus the modern biotechnologists who manipulate DNA are called 'genetic engineers', and aspire to create new organisms as surely as Ferrari creates ever more beautiful motor cars. But there is a series of mistakes in this. First, living organisms are *not* like motor cars.

They were not of our making, and we simply do not and cannot understand them as surely as engineers can understand their own creations. All complex systems in the end are non-linear in their causes and effects but the non-linearity of living organisms outstrips that of any man-made machine by orders of magnitude. But then again, the engineers of Ferrari know full well that even they, with all their precision, cannot make a new car just with the aid of a computer. Once the proto-type is made it must be tested and tested again, in a process very like natural selection—and even when the car is up and running and is obviously wonderful, the testing and improvement continue. There is no such thing as perfection and at any one time some glitch is likely to arise that no one could have foreseen.

In short: the expression 'genetic *engineer*' is deeply deceptive. At best, genetic manipulation is more like gardening, where the gardener pokes at a living system and, in the end, hopes for the best. Secondly, engineers themselves do not control their own creations nearly so well as their biological imitators seem to think they do. Mega-companies and the governments who feel beholden to them queue up to tell us that 'GMOs'– genetically manipulated organisms—meaning crops and livestock, are vital, and are the way forward, and that anyone who says otherwise is a fool. They also assure us that their tests, in computer models and in the field, show that their endeavours are perfectly safe. In truth, GMOs are never vital; after nearly 40 years they have produced nothing of unequivocal value; and the whole operation is run on a wing and a prayer. As more and more effort and resource is invested in GMOs, so more traditional practices that could and have achieved far more are neglected, and vital genetic resources that really could create the crops of the future, are trashed. But in the end the whole grisly exercise is just financial speculation, of the kind that recently brought the world's economy to its knees. But to bring all of agriculture to its knees is folly to the point of wickedness.

One final irony: those who embrace the new biotechnology think, and proclaim, that they are 'modern'; that they represent the future. The people who recognize the value of present-day and traditional approaches, and appreciate what really could be achieved if only we persisted with what is already tried and tested, are dismissed as retrogressives. But philosophically speaking, the thinking behind GM is rooted in the Newtonian, simple cause-and-effect, clockwork universe of the 17th century. The kind of science brought to bear belongs, conceptually, to the 19th century: engineering of the kind so brilliantly carried out—albeit nearly 200 years ago—by Isambard Kingdom Brunel. Or the 'modern' age of biotech may be seen simply as an extension of industrial chemistry, with bells and whistles—and industrial chemistry, too, is a child of the 19th century. The 20th century was truly the age of physics, and changed our whole view of what the world is like and how it really worked (including the ideas of innate uncertainty, and non-linearity). The 21st century *has* to be the Age of Biology—either that, or we will wreck the world entirely, and as it dies, so we will die too. That is true modernity. The present-day 'genetic engineers' who claim the intellectual and the moral high ground and have taken the corporates and governments with them in truth are deeply old-fashioned.

Traditional agriculture was and is, fundamentally, an exercise in applied biology, carried out with proper humility. Traditional farmers, fundamentally, are craftspeople. They have tremendous knowledge. In the past their knowledge was compounded purely from their own experience, and from the experience of many generations of farmers—at least 10,000 years' worth—who had gone before them, and by the time of the Babylonians (at least) had converted many a wild plant and animal into respectable crops and livestock. Life is so complicated, and so non-linear, that there really is no substitute for accumulated experience.

Nowadays, of course—and for the past several hundred years—the traditional knowledge is augmented with science, and invaluable it is too. The traditional techniques are abetted with many an ingenious technology, from windmills to polythene sheeting to computers (which play all kinds of roles). But the science must always be secondary to the craft. What the world needs, in fact, is 'science assisted craft'. This, indeed, is what we had for a time. The supreme example is provided by the plant breeders of the past 250 years or so. As all the world knows, Gregor Mendel in the late 1860s carried out the first experiments that led to the modern science of genetics—growing peas (and other plants too, but peas were the first) in the garden of St Thomas' monastery in Brno, now in the Czech Republic. This was true, quantified science—a clear hypothesis critically tested. Less well known is that, as Newton claimed for himself 200 years earlier, Mendel 'stood on the shoulders of giants'. For the traditional plant breeders of the late 18th and early 19th century were wonderfully sophisticated, and Mendel inherited their skills. The basic structure of his experiments, and the core idea of the 'heritable factor' which was later called the 'gene', were all anticipated—all in the literature; albeit not in any refereed journal of science, for in those days these did not exist.

Plant breeders ever since have continued to build on the traditional craft skills of crossing and selection. Over the course of 10,000 years (at least), craft breeders-cum-farmers turned wild crops into bona-fide crops. Over the past 200 years, craft breeders qua scientists have taken many of these traditional crops to a quite new level. This through a combination of traditional breeding and improved husbandry, the average yield of wheat in Britain has risen from an average of around half a ton per acre—a tonne and a bit per hectare—to around eight tonnes per hectare today. There have been comparable improvements in many other crops. The crude idea that the world stood still before genetic engineering came on board is pure propaganda, mendacious and ignorant. The idea that it could improve significantly on what could be achieved by more craft-based conventional breeding is untested (despite the modern pleas for 'evidence based' agriculture, or medicine, or whatever); and there is very little reason indeed to suppose that it is true. The 'green revolution' of the 1970s, which did achieve significant increases in yields of wheat and rice (though it had a serious downside too) was *not* an exercise in genetic engineering, as is sometimes suggested and commonly supposed. It certainly extended conventional breeding in some most ingenious ways. But still it very clearly belonged to the tradition that began with the pre-Mendelians.

In practice, because of the all-absorbing obsession with cash returns, and the deeply nonsensical and palpably untrue dogma which tells us that the market will solve all, and a deep and horrible misunderstanding of what science really *is* and what it can do, and a huge and overwhelming arrogance where only humility is called for—humility in the face of nature—science this past 150 years has *not* been used to abet the craft. Instead, it has been used to sweep the craft aside, and to replace the traditional farms that worked with rural factories designed to generate wealth and centralize power. Science in general has become the handmaiden of commerce and of big government. All this is crass in the extreme, and it is wicked. At least, it can be forgiven only on grounds of stupidity, 'for they know not what they do'. But stupidity in high places is not forgivable either. A lot of people have been pointing out the shortcomings for decades, and been systematically ignored. Politicians like to claim, when things go horribly wrong, that they 'could not possibly have known'. This was the excuse offered when the banks collapsed recently. But it wasn't for want of telling.

The metaphysics

Do we really need to drag metaphysics into this? Well yes, is the answer—for the reason suggested by Sayyed Hosain Nasr, professor of Islamic Studies at Washington State University (for example in *Man and Nature*, ABC International Group Inc, 1997). Metaphysics, he says, asks the ultimate questions. Science studies what is tangible and measurable, and very necessary it is too—and very beautiful, at its best. But science qua science does not and cannot deal with realities that lie behind what is tangible and measurable what the universe is *really* like. It does not seriously ask 'How come?'—*why* are things the way they are. Why does the universe exist at all?

You may say—well, who needs to contemplate such things, to which the answer is 'Everyone'. In the end, how we perceive the universe and the creatures within it largely determines how we treat them. It is not enough to suggest that we should not fell a tropical rainforest just to make a few dollars (or a few billion dollars) in the short term. It is not enough to make a law to prevent this. If we looked at the world appropriately, if we perceived the innate sacredness of life, if we had some feel for the meaning of hubris, it would not enter our heads to do such a thing. In the same way we do not really need laws to forbid murder. It never enters the heads of most of us that we should actually undertake such a thing (even if we sometimes harbour deep thoughts). Murder has the profundity of taboo; absolutely unthinkable; and taboos spring from our own innate nature, how we really are, and from the *zeitgeist*, the prevailing spirit of the times. In the end it's a matter not of law but of attitude, of worldview; and informing that attitude is a deep sense of sin that lies beyond the musings of moral philosophers, including the sense that life is sacred, and not ours to take. Attitude in the end belongs in the realm of metaphysics; a fundamental idea, a feeling, about what is really important, that springs from a sense of what the universe is really like, and where we fit in it.

In modern western societies metaphysics remains out of sight. It is present in Christianity, which historically has been the favoured western religion, but the word is hardly used in modern contexts and its existence is not stated. Professor Nasr is surely right to suggest that this is a mistake. The disappearance of metaphysics, he says in *Man and Nature* (p 81), is 'most directly responsible for our modern predicament'.

Metaphysics, then, is the indispensable underpinning. It underpins morality in general, and it underpins our attitude to all of nature which in turn, in practice, largely determines how we practice science—for science in the end is a human undertaking, as subject as any other human undertaking to our own preconceptions and emotional input. It should be made explicit.

The only trouble, as Professor Nasr also points out, is that the kinds of questions addressed by metaphysics are often, in practice, addressed in a very disorganized way. Too much organization is stifling, of course, but total freedom to think anything at all gets us nowhere. Metaphysics needs, in short, to be a discipline, as disciplined in its way as any other, with everything thought through that can be thought through.

Once we define the proper *attitude* to life, all else follows. In the end it's the thing that matters most. It should not be left to hazard.

* * * *

As we have seen in early chapters, the farming of future—Real Farming; Enlightened Agriculture—must be based on small to medium-sized, maximally polycultural, low input (quasi-organic) farms which must be labour-intensive precisely because they are so complex. This implies a huge shift of labour, meaning people, back to the land; and a whole new rural economy that is rooted, as is traditional, not in 'horsey-culture' or in conference centres and tourism and all the rest of the stuff that now fills the countryside, but in agriculture. In other words, we need a 'New Agrarianism'.

The New Agrarianism

Whenever somebody (like me) suggests that we need to get people back on to the land, en masse and as quickly as possible, people who in truth know nothing of rural life (although they may have weekend cottages) or of agriculture and know no history to speak of, rush to assure us all that country life is not, as woolly-heads (like me) suppose, all that it has been cracked up to be. People who live and work on small farms suffer, and always have. As they say in China: 'Peasants have their back to the sun, and their face to the earth'. Even in rich Britain, small farmers are often desperately poor, and head for head they have the highest suicide rate of any trade. So too in comfortable New Zealand. In parts of the Third World (Punjab, South Korea) suicide in farmers is epidemic. Only a townee (like me) could possibly suppose that it's fun to bring lambs into the world at 3 o' clock on a February morning. Life on the small farm is, in short, as Thomas Hobbes said of human life in general, 'solitary, poor, nasty, brutish, and short'. Indeed, one zealous adviser to the agro-chemical industry opined in a review of my previous book (*So Shall We Reap*) that his employers were doing the farmers a favour by throwing them off the land. The British Treasury mandarins who argued through the 1980s and '90s (though less so now) that British farming should go the way of its coal-mining supported their case partly on moral grounds. Farming was too awful a job for any civilized society to tolerate. Then again, country living raises huge logistic problems. It is hard to organize schools for rural children. Cut off, rural people tend to turn into hicks and rednecks. Clearly they would be more fulfilled in cities (and leave their country idylls for rich city folk to commute to).

Recently, too, in this age of greenwash, we have seen articles from food industry hacks (who surely do not realize how they have been gulled) that rural life is a terrible drain on the economy, and (paradoxically) on the environment. Transport is more difficult when people are far apart; houses are harder to keep warm when they do not huddle in terraces and tower-blocks; and so on.

To be sure, country life and particularly farming life *has* often been harsh to the point of intolerable, and still often is. When people are scattered far and wide there are logistic problems of many kinds—transport in general; medical care; schooling. But none of this is inevitable. Things are as they are because this is the way the powers-that-be have organized things—and the rest of us have allowed them to get away with it.

Small farmers the world over are desperately poor mostly because at every turn the economic dice are loaded against them. In Europe and the US it's the big farmers who get the lion's share of the subsidies (and the subsidies themselves are a serious bending of the neoliberal rules that are supposed to apply to all of us; and serve to tip the balance of the much-vaunted 'competition' even more decisively in favour of those who already have the advantage). The rich grow richer and the poor grow poorer. Under the rules of the free market the prices of crops are not fixed in advance except by special contract and without fixed prices for their produce Third World farmers cannot risk investing in the inputs that would increase their yields—and so they stay poor, and politicians conclude that they are unproductive (and poor) because they are 'backward'. Laws and restrictions of all kinds that are doubtless necessary for the big factory farms are applied with equal zeal to small farms where they often are not relevant at all. I have never heard small farmers complain about birthing sheep—they tend to refer to their nights on the hills with pride. But I have seen them bowed down with ludicrous paper work. In Britain at least the network of local abattoirs and shops that once served small farmers now no longer exists. The small greengrocers and butchers that once were content to take a few lambs or cabbages at a time are now replaced with a few supermarkets, who don't deal in less than truckloads.

Above all, urban-based societies—or at least, those like Britain that have also lost their food culture—pay far too little for food. Politicians make a virtue of this. At the start of 2010 Britain's then Secretary of State for food and farming, Hilary Benn, boasted that Britons now spend only 11 per cent of their income on food. That, he obviously thought, was a good thing. When French food was at its height (alas, it is now losing out to industrialization) the French spent 30 per cent of their income on food—and, although they had other problems, there was no jollier society anywhere. Food culture is the centre of civilization. Again, though, the powers-that-be are self-righteous. If food was dearer, they say, the poor could not afford it.

Nobody pointed out that the average working Brit now spends half of his or her income on their mortgage, almost all of which goes to bankers—although houses are not that expensive to build, and should be readily available to all. In practice, indeed, in countries like Britain, most of us spend *most* of our income on taxes and on bankers. The housing market ensures that the largest possible slice of people's earnings finishes up with the bankers. It is, in fact, a scam. The food industry is a scam, too, though of a slightly different kind. The housing scam is intended to ensure that houses are as dear as possible, and so is the direct cause of injustice and inequity on a huge and systemic scale; and the food scam is as cheap as possible, to ensure that no one obviously starves as a result.

In short, the two industries that stand at the centre of all our lives, that provide us with our life-support system, are both obvious scams. We should be angry about the price of houses because they are so ludicrously expensive, for reasons that are all to do with the power and enrichment of a minority. We should be angry about the price of food in Britain because it is—or is dressed up to seem as if it is—so ludicrously cheap, again for reasons that are entirely to do with the enrichment of the few; although much of what we do spend on food goes to the bankers too, as the farmers and retailers strive to pass off their debts. We should not be rejoicing, as we are invited to rejoice, that the poor can afford to eat. We should be asking why it is that in countries like Britain and the United States, which are so rich, and see themselves as models for the rest to follow, there are so many poor people.

What we need, as all modern people need, are the kind of government and an economy which, as Abraham Lincoln put the matter in a slightly different context, are 'by the people and for the people'. But as things are, given the power of the banks and corporates and the perceived need of modern governments to support them at all costs, this is not going to happen. We need a different kind of world, and we need it quickly, because the world itself, the fabric of the Earth and the life it supports, are being trashed. But we cannot look to the powers that be to supply it. The corporates and banks, and the governments that support them, are not focused on the issues. It follows that if we give a damn, then we, people at large, Ordinary Joes, have to do the job ourselves. How?

CHAPTER 6

The Campaign for Real Farming

Government 'for the people' means that we should not be content with present injustice—with incomes so unequal that some, apparently, cannot afford to buy good food, and many cannot afford a good house, while a very few are ludicrously rich, to the obvious detriment of the rest of us. Specifically it means, among other things, that we have to take rural life, and agriculture, seriously, as recent governments, at least in Britain and similar countries, have not done for some time.

To be sure, as we saw in the last chapter, rural life—agrarian living—raises its own problems, logistic and technical. But they are all there to be solved; and there are technologies galore out there that could solve them, or at least are ready and waiting. Isolated houses are in principle more difficult to heat—but if there is plenty of space all around, as by definition there is if the house is isolated, they can be beautifully insulated, which is by far the most important thing to get right. There are examples of eco-houses all around the world that look very good and are not expensive (their two-foot thick cavity walls are filled with fire-proofed straw), and remain pleasantly cool in summer and can be warmed even in the harshest winters virtually with a 150 watt bulb. (I exaggerate slightly, but not much). Small farms are necessary but it is becoming increasingly hard to buy appropriate machinery—100-plus horsepower tractors are easier to come by than 30 horsepower tractors. Yet it is just as easy, in principle, to tailor machinery and everything else that's needed to the small farm, as it is to build for vast estates. It's just a question of wanting to do it. It is harder to provide on-the-spot medical care and schools for people who live in the country—but becomes far easier as the rural communities are re-established; and in any case, since we need proper farming communities, these problems are worth spending money on. With the internet, no one these days has to be a hick. You can work in the middle of nowhere and still log on to the Bodleian library and read for your external D Phil (or I presume you can, and if you can't, it's not for lack of technology).

Overall, we need to re-visit and take seriously the advice of Ivan Illich and E F ('Fritz') Schumacher. Illich in the 1960s and onwards pointed out that while some technologies truly make life easier, and are liberating, others merely ensure that powerful people increase their power over the rest of us. Illich argued that the prime desideratum, for individuals and for their societies, is autonomy: our freedom to shape our own lives. Technologies that increase autonomy he called 'Tools for Conviviality'—the title of his seminal book of 1973. Writing when he did, he proposed the bicycle and the telephone as prime exemplars of convivial technologies—both tending to increase the personal freedom and scope of individuals, without the intervention and the meddling of governments. Nowadays we might suggest that the internet is outstandingly convivial—and might observe that ID cards and DNA data-bases, say, are prime examples of technology expressly designed to centralize power. In the context of food and agriculture, the small tractor and local plant breeding are convivial. GM and mega-combines for vast estates are all about the consolidation of power.

Schumacher's best-known book was called *Small is Beautiful*, emphasizing above all the need to scale the technology to the real needs of people and of the world. Key to his thesis is the idea of 'appropriate technology'. Often the most appropriate technology is traditional—'low-tech'. A well-designed harness on an ox cart can solve a myriad of problems. But we need not assume that the most appropriate technologies are necessarily low-tech. The mobile phone, the internet, the on-farm solar panel, and the many novel forays into biological pest control are prime examples of high-tech that is very appropriate indeed—although to be truly appropriate, and to meet Illich's criterion of autonomy the means of production must be in the hands of the people. (You don't have to be a fully paid-up Marxist to borrow Illich's ideas. But Marx was a considerable moralist as well as an economist).

All in all, it is obvious that we need to do things very differently, and to think very differently. It is also obvious that the powers-that-be have no intention of changing their ways—because they have not understood the problems, because they are convinced that what they are doing is right, because they would find it very hard to change direction even if they wanted to, and because they don't want to change in any radical ways because they are doing very nicely out of the status quo, thank you very much. Of course, modern governments and big business like to give the impression that they are making changes, because it justifies their existence. They fear that if they simply left things alone then the rest of us would ask, what are they really *for*? But some of the greatest leaders of history have been content to do as little as possible. Whatever they do or don't do, however, the modern powers-that-be would never do anything that compromised their own ascendancy.

To repeat: It follows that if we give a damn then we, all of us, Ordinary Joes, just have to do what needs doing ourselves. This in truth applies to almost all aspects of our lives in all contexts, including education and medicine. In the context of food and agriculture we need nothing less than 'A people's takeover of the world's food supply'. How?

A people's takeover of the world's food supply

In principle there are three possible ways to bring about political, economic, and social change: by Reform; by Revolution; or by Renaissance.

Reform means in practice that we try to persuade the powers-that-be, whoever the powers-that-be may be, to change their ways. In practice, reform of a kind happens continuously. Governments seek to change the status quo all the time, or at least to appear to do so.

On the specifics of food and farming, I seem to have been to more meetings than is good for anyone with titles like, 'Whither the Common Agricultural Policy?'—in which civil servants and the odd invited professor seek to twiddle with Europe's Byzantine farming strategy, and the occasional government minister drops in for a harangue (and rapidly out again, en route to something more important).

Reform can doubtless be useful up to a point. Bad laws and inappropriate taxes can be rescinded ad hoc. But reform alone can achieve only so much. Radical thinking is needed, and the civil servants and professors who attend respectable international meetings are not equipped to think radically. They have no remit to do so, and for the most part, they don't know enough. Their brief is to make things better, or look better, without disturbing the present power-structure, or offending the dogma of neoliberalism. They cannot even begin to do the kinds of things that are really needed. They are obliged to operate within the *zeitgeist*. But we need a new *zeitgeist*: what the American philosopher Thomas Kuhn called a 'paradigm shift'.

Revolutions can achieve a great deal quickly but they raise huge problems of their own. Typically, the collateral damage is enormous. Always, valuable and sometimes vital babies are thrown out with the bathwater. The outcome is always uncertain. Of course, cause and effect in human societies are innately non-linear, so political action of any kind—or any kind of social intervention—is always unpredictable in its outcome. But revolutions happen so quickly and tend to be so cavalier that the uncertainty is multiplied ten-fold. Did the revolutionaries of Russia in 1917 foresee Stalin? Did the followers of Mao anticipate that China would triumph economically by adopting the trappings of corporate capitalism? At this stage of history the world and its people and all other creatures are too precariously placed to risk the kind of upheaval that revolution brings. We need radical change, and fast, but we need to stay in control of events, at least as far as possible.

Renaissance is the only way left—and by far the most promising. Surely, indeed, it is the way forward. Literally, of course, renaissance means 're-birth'. Nothing is more radical than birth. A whole new life comes into being. But birth itself, even the birth of great prophets, is not usually dramatic in itself. The Gospels tell us that the birth of Jesus Christ did draw some attention, from shepherds and magi and eventually from the powers-that-be in the form of Herod. But no historians of the time apart from the gospel-makers seem to have noticed it, and the gospels themselves emphasize the essential lowliness: he was born in a stable. Yet this birth was at least in retrospect the most significant event in historical times. (Muslims need have no quarrel with this. Mohammed says much the same thing).

Renaissance in the present context does not require the birth of a prophet. It can and should be brought about by the means that gave rise to the Italian Renaissance from the 15th century onwards, which changed Western Europe so absolutely, and so changed the whole world. Groups of people just started doing things differently. In Renaissance Italy the changes were brought about by rich families deciding to do their own thing, of whom the Medicis are the best known. In the present world, as a matter of urgency, we need Agrarian Renaissance—and this must be brought about by 'ordinary people', everywhere, in all walks of life, just deciding to do things differently. In this Renaissance, all of us have a part to play, starting now.

In truth the Agrarian Renaissance is already happening. All around the world individuals and small groups are making new things happen, of a kind that with a following wind could still save the world, even at this late hour; and all we need really ask of governments and the rest of the powers-that-be is that they should stay out of the way. Of course if governments were actively to *help*, with grants and tax-breaks and changes of law, then that would be good. It would be good in general if governments were truly on the side of people at large, and used our money, tax-payers money, for things that were actually good for us. But their active involvement is not vital. So long as governments don't actively obstruct, then good things can start to happen; and if there are enough good things, then we, people-at-large, could soon form a critical mass that could do what is now so desperately needed.

So what kinds of things can be done, and who is doing what?

What needs to be done

Radical change is needed and to achieve this we need to begin from first principles and re-think *everything*. I have found that many practical people are impatient with theoretical musing, and I sympathize with this. But movements that can truly change society and the world need to have the deepest and broadest possible roots and, I suggest, we really do need, collectively, to identify and re-think all the vital principles that underlie and provide the framework for the practicalities: the economy; the possible contributions of science; the kinds of technology required; the political structure; the morality (what *should* we be trying to do?); the aesthetics (don't we care what it all looks like, and tastes like?); and the metaphysics (what is the world really like, and why should we give a damn in the first place?); all of which we outlined in broad terms in earlier chapters.

But while all that thinking is going on, we, people at large, also need to be doing practical things: making the Renaissance happen, literally, on the ground. Action is needed on every front. This includes:

Farmers and land

It still isn't clear how many farmers the world really needs—and clearly the number will vary from country to country, depending on various realities such as the nature of the landscape and the economic circumstances and history. Adam Smith in the 18th century expressly asked, 'What is the proper ratio of urban to rural workers?'—how many farmers do we really need? Indeed this is a vital question for research—there is none more fundamental—but like virtually all matters that are truly important, it seems to be completely neglected at government or international level. At least, I know of no state-sponsored research to explore this issue (and if anyone does, please do get in touch).

We might reasonably suggest, however, at least to begin the discussion, that even in the most industrialized countries, at least one working person in ten should be a farmer. In other words, it would become the task of each farming family to cater for ten other, non-farming families. But for most countries, industrialization to the degree that we see in Britain and the US are not a realistic option, and it would be very good for the world if we all faced up to this. Britain achieved its industrial might by garnering resources and labour from around the world, and still contrives to do so. So does the US, as it draws in immigrant labour and battles, literally, to command the world's oil. But there is only one world, and acquisitiveness on such a scale is unrepeatable. The well-worn cliché has it that for everyone to live like the average Brit would require the resources of three planets Earth, and for all to live like the upper echelons of California would require 10 planets Earth, or indeed an infinite number, since the aspiration is infinite. So although some countries certainly need to become more industrialized, most must above all emphasize and develop their agrarian base for the simple and inescapable reason that there is no realistic alternative—not, that is, if we truly care about the people as a whole, and our fellow creatures, and are not prepared to dedicate our lives and the world to the wealth and aggrandisement of the few.

But, we might really suggest, no country of any kind—not even the most agrarian—should ideally employ more than 50 per cent of its labour in agriculture. In such societies each farming family would cater for only one other family. But if more than half were on the land in any one country, then there would not be not enough people to do all the other jobs that are vital for a convivial life—doctors, nurses, teachers, builders, plumbers, cooks, artists, musicians, and so on. Neither are there enough non-farmers in over-agrarian societies to buy the food that the farmers produce, so the farmers cannot market their produce and never move beyond subsistence. 'The new agrarianism' implies that we should take farming seriously. It does not imply that anyone should work all the hours that God made just to keep body and soul together (unless this is what particular individuals choose to do).

In reality, 'developed' countries—which in general are those of the West—have far fewer people on the land than the so-called

'developing' countries, collectively known as 'the Third World'.
Today, indeed, with our perverted economy, the countries with the
fewest farmers are considered to be the most 'advanced', and countries who retain a significant proportion of farmers are held to be
'backward—in want of westernization. In Rwanda, 90 per cent of
the workforce is on the land. To be sure we can conclude that 90
per cent is too many—the remaining 10 per cent provide virtually
no market for the 90 per cent. So observers and Rwandans alike can
reasonably agree that more alternative industry in Rwanda would
be a good thing.

In starkest contrast, in Britain and the United States only about
one per cent of the workforce now works full time on the land (although the numbers in both cases are swelled by immigrants, Mexi-
can or Polish or Romanian or whoever is poorest at the time, but
the immigrants, vital though they are, are not generally factored in.
In truth, these two beacons of modernity and civilization run their
agriculture largely on the black economy, or at least conveniently
grey). The dramatic reduction in the farm labour force in those countries is taken as a sure sign of modernity. In truth, though, Britain
and the US have gone way out on a limb, and have so few competent farmers left that serious agriculture—the enlightened kind that
is actually intended to feed people—is becoming all but impossible.
As the oil dwindles and the big machines are grounded, and the
world warms up and the landscape changes and new approaches
are required, farming designed expressly to feed people will become
absolutely vital. But the countries with the hyper-industrialized agriculture will not be able to change course—not least, as is already
evident, because they will have lost all their farming skills. Rwanda
is far better placed to face the future. It may need to halve its rural
workforce. But Britain (and the US), as a matter of urgency, need to
increase their farming workforce by at least 10 times to bring it up
to the minimum safe and sensible level.

Countries like India have 60 per cent on the land—which is
roughly the Third World average. Accordingly, the western powers-
that-be, and the westernized powers-that-be within India, urge it to
go the way of the US and Britain and industrialize—and so it has

been doing, for the most part, as fast as this could be arranged. As things are, conventional wisdom has it, India is 'under-developed'—as demonstrated by its masses of poor farmers. Yet in truth, India is more or less on course. It probably needs to shed a few more—50 per cent rather than 60 per cent—but no more than that. People who really care about India and its people should not be trying to get rid of its farmers. It should simply be trying to help them—and not necessarily by changing what they do but by ensuring that they are properly paid for what they do. Indeed, industrialization of agriculture leading to mass elimination of farmers would be—and already is—disastrous. It is hard to imagine that those politicians and industrialists who are urging industrialization have ever seen the slums of Old Delhi or Mumbai, or Hyderabad, or almost anywhere. *This*, not the city streets of uptown Manhattan and the City of London, is the real alternative to farming, at least for the foreseeable future. Turkey, with 30 per cent on the land, should thank its lucky stars that it seems to have been excluded from the European Union, which was demanding huge reduction. Turkey's crowning glory is its food and farming, and the communities that go with them, and to sacrifice this for a few more Mercedes-Benz and prestige commercial architecture would be the greatest tragedy.

So—just to start the discussion at home—how is Britain to raise its farming workforce from one per cent to ten per cent? How can it bring about a 10-fold increase? With difficulty, is the answer, but if we approach it step by step we can see that it is far from impossible.

Overall, of course, Britain needs serious land-reform. At present, 35,000 people own half of all of the land in England and Wales—which is somewhat less than one thousandth of the whole population. Much of that land, including much of the most fertile land, is simply playground, increasingly for the daughters of bankers and lawyers to keep their ponies, and the bankers themselves to land their helicopters. But even in the short term, in the absence of serious reform, we need to make it far easier than it is for people to get back to the land. At present, it is very difficult indeed.

We can approach this problem from two angles. First, we should look at ways of making land available. Secondly, we should seek to create a plausible career path for would-be farmers. Since most of the farmers we need are now working in the city, and may be five generations removed from any farm, this path in practice will be quite long.

Making land available

Despite the underlying inequity, and the absence of worthwhile government, many initiatives are in train to help to fulfill the first requirement—to make land more available. In Britain, for example, there is a growing cadre of enlightened landlords who actively seek to involve people at large. A near-ish neighbour of mine in South Oxfordshire with 800 acres is letting out some of his land for allotments—and, he says, if any of the allotmenteers prove particularly keen or adept, he would certainly consider allowing them to take over more and become tenant smallholders, and after that, who knows? In the village of Martin on the borders of Hampshire and Wiltshire Nick Snelgar and his fellow villagers are renting 20 acres from the local landowner and running it *themselves*, as a mixed holding. The village farm has poultry, pigs, sheep, and now a microdairy. The villagers largely or mostly commute to work, but they take it in turns to feed the chickens before they set off, and lock them up when they get home, and no one has ever defaulted. The enterprise is planning to employ a professional manager but at present the only full-time pro runs the vegetable plot, which provides the whole village. A vital adjunct is the farm shop in the village hall, selling the produce, and again run by the villagers. The enterprise is branded, 'Future Farms'—and the future it could indeed be. (Further details of all the places mentioned in this chapter—or at least, details of a website that will lead you to them all—are given later).

There are many more such examples of private landowners who positively encourage community involvement and so long as landowners behave in this enlightened fashion, I for one would be happy if they stayed put. Responsible land management is not easy, and in practice many of the world's best-run estates are privately owned, and so long as they deliver what society needs, then fair enough. There are huge practical problems, however. One is that landlords these days are very reluctant to offer long-term contracts. Real farms take years to establish, and should improve over decades. Farmers ideally, including tenant farmers, should be able to contemplate a lifetime in situ if they choose. Nowadays, for various reasons, tenancies are offered only for a year at a time—or, in practice, just for 11 months. One reason is the ever-pending presence of land speculators, anxious to snaffle all the land they can for building. Good farmland at present in Britain costs an enormous £5000 up to £10,000 per acre, but the value can easily rise a hundred-fold once permission is granted to build. With 11 months to play with a farmer can graze his sheep or plant and harvest a crop of this, that, or the other but cannot establish a serious, integrated, ever-improving farm. Again we see how present laws, and the present economy, are the enemies of good farming.

Also, and obviously, benign landlords don't live forever, and their successors may not be enlightened. At best, with traditional landlords, the lives and wellbeing of entire communities depend on the whim of a single individual, and that is surely not ideal. If the land is bought by some tycoon, perhaps holed out somewhere in the Caribbean, as a hedge against inflation, then the whole arrangement evaporates: and this, in today's world, is the way of things. The present economy is vile beyond belief. As far as can be seen, in this vaunted democracy of ours, it has absolutely nothing to do with the general wellbeing of the people, or the state of the world at large, and everything to do with the enrichment of speculators. But the economic status quo is sanctified by law, both national and international, and is solemnly underwritten by a succession of elected governments. No wonder we are in a mess.

It is more satisfactory, at least in principle, if the land is owned by some benevolent trust that is *not* a part of some family's inheritance, or a component of some ex-pat's financial portfolio. Two examples known to me are the Northmoor Trust in Oxfordshire and the Dartington estate in Devon, both of which are inviting would-be farmers to come and farm. The Church of England and the various colleges of the universities of Oxford and Cambridge are among Britain's major landowners who could, if they chose, initiate similar schemes.

More generally, people who give a damn could pool their pennies and create a 'Fund for Enlightened Agriculture' (aka the 'Fund for Real Farming'). The fund would buy land specifically for farming that is intended to provide good food for everybody, and good jobs, without wrecking the rest of the world. In the same way, in Britain, the Royal Society for the Protection of Birds acquires land to conserve bird habitats (and individual species), and the Woodland Trust buys and restores ancient woods, and the National Trust takes care of entire landscapes and the buildings within them. In short, there are precedents for the Fund for Real Farming. Of course, the Fund for Real Farming could and should overlap the existing organizations. Farming in practice can be a fruitful part of all landscapes.

Finally, we are witnessing the growth of 'Community Supported Agriculture', or CSAs. These take various forms but one common model is for a community simply to employ local farmers to supply them with food—requiring the farmers to farm to high standards of welfare and so on, but also providing a guaranteed market, and enabling the farmers to break away from the treadmill of monoculture and supermarkets. CSAs can exist on any scale. Box schemes are a form of CSA. Or CSAs can own the land and rent it to farmers, and sometimes do. Various initiatives within Britain's growing 'Transition Town' movement encourage local, enlightened farming and most could so a lot more than they do. There are nettles here to be grasped.

The career path: from city to farm

On the website that I and my wife, Ruth, and a few friends have set up—of which more later—is an essay that describes 'eight steps back to the land'. I won't spell it out in detail here but the point is that we can envisage such a path—by which people who now work in cities and have never in their lives given a serious thought to the countryside could, step by step, metamorphose into farmers. The order of play can vary somewhat but the general gist is as follows:

Step one is just to take food seriously. Without being any kind of grower yourself, you can just start to be a discriminating consumer— for example, by buying only what's in season, and getting as much as possible from local farmers, for example at farmers' markets. Stage two is to start growing yourself—first in a window-box if that's all you've got. Then—stage three—graduate to an allotment. Stage four is to scale up. Stage five is to start to incorporate small livestock— meaning omnivores, beginning with poultry and perhaps graduating to pigs and/or goats. This is a huge conceptual leap because animals need serious looking after. It's a shame to neglect plants and lose the crop but to neglect animals is a sin. Stage six is to start selling the produce. Stage seven is to become a part-time farmer—at this stage, perhaps, incorporating grazing, or small-arable, and raising the serious herbivores, which mostly in Britain means goats, sheep, and cattle. Stage eight is to become a full-time farmer.

I particularly like the idea of stage seven. The world needs full time professionals of course but in practice, part-time farmers are vital if the world is ever to be well-fed, and people at large are ever to get the best out of life. Integrated, mixed farms require enormous amounts of work—all the hours that God made, at some times of year—but individual enterprises can always be part-time. Sheep re-quire 24-hour care when lambing—but for much of the year they more or less take care of themselves. Dairy farming is enormously demanding—but it is perfectly possible to milk only once a day and allow the cow to raise her own calf, for the calf requires only half of the milk (or less) provided by a modern, well-fed dairy animal. Unlikely though it may seem, too, there is a strong case to be made on welfare grounds alone for robotic milking machines. Here is high tech in truly 'convivial' form, which *could* be scaled down for the small farmer.

A part-time farmer is surely a good thing to be—indeed it offers the best of all worlds. Many part-time farmers are also teachers, or accountants, or doctors, or builders, or what you will—and this has always been the case. John Adams, one of the founders of the modern United States, was a lawyer and a statesman—but also a farmer. He was typical of his day. Indeed the person he took most exception to—Britain's George III—was known as Farmer George; and a very good farmer he was too, in his periods of sanity. In our own time, Britain's Prince Charles is an accomplished gardener, too, and a knowledgeable agriculturalist. Third-world farmers are often part-timers. Scotland's crofters, who have been a huge part of Highland life, and should continue to be so, were traditionally part-timers, and for the most part still are. All the Italians I have ever met seem to have olive groves tucked away somewhere, or their uncle has, and they rush off in due season for the harvest. Italian footballers playing for English clubs have been known to make frantic phone-calls at half time to ask after the olives. Germany's hobby-farmers are part-timers. The Russian dacha is not, traditionally, just a week-end cottage. It is a smallholding, run by ordinary Russians as well as by the rich. Britain's allotments could in principle upgrade into dachas. Of course, in Britain, planning laws get in the way. People who work on their small farms for a weekend at a time need a place to stay, and housing that does not generate huge piles of cash is frowned upon. But all the part-timers need most of the time are ad hoc dwellings, from caravans to yurts to custom-built and beauteous chalets. It's all out there waiting to be done. We have to make part-time farming work. Worldwide, part-timers make a crucial contribution to the world's food economy.

Tony Blair, as he presided over the further decline of Britain's farming begun by earlier governments, suggested that full-time farmers should 'diversify'. He meant they should turn their farms in to B&Bs, or send their spouses out to work; in either case, he urged them to subsidize the meagre returns now achievable from farming with still greater efforts, and hence to subsidize the nation's food, and foster the illusion that food is cheap and that the government is in control and has the people's best interests at heart. Part-time farming in effect achieves the same end-result—but it does so more honestly, and it leaves the farmer in charge of his or her own life. Part-time farmers do indeed supplement their own farming income with another job, but they do it on their own terms. They are not panicking, as the full-time farmer-cum-hotelier is, just to keep the home fires burning. A half-way competent government, or one that was half-way alert, would be encouraging part-time farming. It could do this on social grounds alone, even if it didn't take the food supply seriously. But the path to part-time farming can be trodden without government help, provided the government keeps out of the way. Even so, a few tax adjustments and tweaks of the planning laws would help.

Finally, all the problems can be eased if farmers form co-operatives. In some countries (Denmark and Northern Italy come to mind) co-operatives are the norm. In Britain, farmers often seem to find it hard to co-operate. But there are some excellent co-operative ventures even here. When farmers work together they increase their own security (and their bargaining power) no end.

Still the doubters ask—but do enough people really want to go back to the land? Surely people prefer the cities? I've often heard it said—not least by old farmers—that 'young people just don't want to know'. Farming is too hard. Surely that's why people worldwide are leaving the land in droves!

Well, I seem to meet people all the time in their 20s and 30s who would love to be farmers. They would relish the physical hardships—far preferring them to the horrors of commuting on some grid-locked bypass, or the London Underground, or some mindless job in a call-centre. The real hardships of present-day farming—the poverty, insecurity, the lack of kudos, the often nonsensical form-filling—are all caused by the particular circumstance of our day— by societies that simply have got their priorities wrong, and have devised an economic system that makes it very hard indeed to earn a living by farming well. Farmers are leaving the land in droves (half a billion rural people have been citified in China, a thousand farmers a month are still being lost in Britain even though there are precious few remaining) just because agrarian life has been made so difficult, not because it is intrinsically impossible. Contrariwise, it is immensely difficult to get back to the land. To be sure, whenever anyone points out that many people would love to get back to the land, some city-based defender of the status quo will be bound to point out that this is just illusion, a dream of some never-existent rural idyll. But for many people it is not an illusion. It is what they want to do, and would be good at. I have met many who have already made the break, and who feel their life did not begin until they threw off the shackles of the city. It should be obvious, too, that many of the country people who dream of the city are at least as deluded. A billion worldwide now live in urban slums—which means that nearly one in three city people now live in slums. Is this what is meant by 'progress'?

As for the farmers' lack of kudos—well: it doesn't have to be like that. In many societies farmers have always been highly respected; and the transformation of modern Cuba shows how quickly perceptions can be changed. America left Cuba's farming in a dreadful state—dedicated in effect to monocultural plantation crops, including maize. The Russians then helped out with oil but withdrew after 1989, leaving Cuba isolated and desperate. So the Cubans started growing their own food. Havana has become a miracle of productivity. Growers are in demand—suddenly among the best-respected, most highly-valued members of society, up there with doctors (who of course in Cuba are of very high standard). I remember a (filmed) interview with a former computer executive who gave up his lucrative city life to grow vegetables and says he feels that that is when his life really began. Just make the job tolerable by removing the obvious obstacles, and after that, perception is all.

Marketing

I am using the term 'marketing' broadly, to include all the steps that may take place between the farmer and the customer: distribution; preparation—including butchery, brewing, and baking; and retail. Without good marketing, farming is dead in the water—and that is just as true of tomorrow's enlightened farms, as it is of the industrial monocultures that prevail today. But the marketing chain we have now—mega-abattoirs; huge trucks traversing countries and continents; huge ships and even planes ferrying megatons of produce across oceans; everything geared to the centralised depot and the supermarket—is quite unsuited to the needs of enlightened farming. So we need a quite new food chain. Like farming itself, it must be designed by the people and for the people—and for the world at large: and it will not come into being unless people who give a damn, Ordinary Joes, make it happen. Governments have lost the plot—in effect have abdicated, although they still occupy their respective premises.

Again we see a whole range of possibilities already in action worldwide, There are box schemes, in which customers order what they want and the farmer puts it all in a box to be collected. There are farmers' markets, generally run weekly or monthly or somewhere in between, which the farmers attend themselves. There are farm shops. Food hubs are developing apace too: central distribution points where local farmers take their produce as and when and customers order on line. There are some small, locally-run and locally owned and highly efficient supermarkets, combining the convenience of the commercial supermarket (credit where it's due) with the far greater advantages of fresh local produce and local control. Paradoxically (perhaps) the lead country in this counter-insurgency is the United States—source of some of the world's ghastliest political and economic thinking but also, still, the natural seed-bed of truly innovative thinking.

Still extant too, just about, are the traditional retail stores—grocers, greengrocers, high-street butchers, bakers, and micro-brewers. All of them raise immense logistic problems of the same general kind as beset enlightened farmers—the national and the global economy is not geared to them. Rents can be prohibitively high; bureaucracy that is relevant to supermarkets and food factories is applied with equal zeal to small businesses, for whom the cost may be crippling; and so on. Again, all of these essential enterprises can in principle be run by communities, often run as cooperatives using the CSA as a model. People working together can achieve anything. The supply of food and all that goes with it may seem to be sewn up. The corporates, supported by elected governments, are indeed immensely powerful. But the game is not over.

As with farming, the marketing (broadly defined) needs to be thought through in detail and the details acted upon but it's not my area of expertise so I can add very little that is original. But I would like to cite and recommend the endeavours of Tim Waygood, at Church Farm in Hertfordshire, to the north of London, who has established a company and a movement that he calls, in a no-nonsense way, 'Agrarian Renaissance'. Church Farm is 170 acres—modest in size by today's standards, although quite large enough for an excellent, mixed farm—and it is Tim's principal if not his sole source of income so it *has* to pay its way, supporting the family and a staff that by today's standards, is large. He achieves all this firstly by making the farm extremely interesting—beautiful Red Poll suckler cattle (the cows raising their own calves), sheep, Berkshire pigs (and other breeds), arable crops, vegetables, orchards with livestock, trees with plans for bona-fide agro-forestry, and plans also for aqua-culture. All this by itself, of course, is not enough to guarantee commercial success. He succeeds by making the farm a true centre of the community. He has a shop to supply produce from his own farm—which also stocks the kinds of things that everyone needs day-to-day, from soap to matches, so that customers can get all they need in one trip, as they do to a supermarket. He aims to supply 200 customers regularly—enough, he suggests, to keep a farm like his going. The farm is also perceived as a kind of country park, where people can come for walks and picnics and to spend weekends. The customers are also invited to become subscribers, with annual membership, won back by discounts in the shop; an excellent newsletter; the freedom to visit the farm; and events. Thus, as a business, Church Farm is a form of CSA. Others could emulate his model, says Tim. He aims to roll the model out as a social franchise. In the not too distant future there could be something similar in each county. After that—who knows? Here, surely, is exactly the kind of enterprise that could be the start of something quite new—and far, far better for people at large and for the world.

Food culture

Systematically, this past 40 years, most noticeably in Britain and the United States but even, too, shamefully, in all the countries that were havens of great cooking from France and Italy to India and China, food culture has been systematically undermined. It has been replaced by 'standard products' and fast food, essentially high-tech, controlled by big companies and run primarily for profit. In some societies of Britain family meals have all but disappeared, although the shared meal is the traditional centre of family life. Huge propaganda has accompanied the shift—promulgated of course by the big food companies but supported, inevitably, by modern governments, often (paradoxically) in the name of political correctness. In the 1970s, in Britain, 'domestic science', then known as 'home economics', was dropped from school curricula because it was seen to be sexist (apparently), even though boys did it too.

Yet cooking can be the great liberator. In principle it is the individual's opportunity to do his or her own thing. In the kitchen, cooks create. A good cook can summon great meals from the simplest ingredients—provided the ingredients are wholesome in the first place. As noted earlier, great cooking and real farming go perfectly together—indeed they need each other: the future really does belong to the gourmet. Some of the best cooking is still to be had (although it's disappearing fast) in some of the world's poorest societies—because it is based on local produce and the small, local farmers are generally poor. But it is not romantic nonsense—it is simply, obviously the case—that people who can eat well are never truly poor, in any worthwhile sense. People on the other hand who earn £100,000 a year but work all hours and never see an uninterrupted sunset except on their annual package holiday and live, most of the time, on ready meals of standard industrial varieties snatched from the supermarket, are very poor indeed. But the latter, in this perverse world, is seen to represent 'progress'. It does after all create huge piles of wealth for the corporates who run the whole show, while governments are content to tot up their wealth and call it GDP.

Yet again, we see fight-back on all fronts. Pub and restaurant food has certainly improved in Britain this past few years, with more and more local sourcing. Micro-breweries and bakeries have sprung up, sometimes community owned and run. The Slow Food Movement, based in Italy but with global ambitions, campaigns vigorously and effectively for food culture. Its international food fairs held biennially in Turin are a treat, and hugely important. In Britain the Campaign for Real Ale is well established and the Campaign for Real Bread is growing apace. Many individuals worldwide are beginning to do the job that was once done in schools—teaching the rest of us how to cook; and schools are beginning to re-introduce cooking and gardening (and sometimes even farming).

Research by individuals

In the early 1970s I worked for *Farmer's Weekly* and wrote largely about Britain's agricultural research. For several years running in the early 1980s I wrote the scientific section of the Agricultural and Food Research Council's annual report. So I spent time at all 30 or so of Britain's government-supported research stations and a fabulous network it was, providing a continuing stream of new insights into all aspects of agriculture, most of it for home consumption but much of it relevant the world over, plus a host of new crops that got better and better as the years passed. Further downstream was a network of Experimental Husbandry Farms which did what their name suggests: tried out new ways of doing things, to see what worked. The information was passed directly to Britain's farmers.

But in the early 1970s the government of the day commissioned Lord Rothschild to report on the state of British agricultural research and he came up with the 'customer-contractor' principle, which said in effect that apart from a few core projects, research into farming should be undertaken only if some 'customer' said they wanted it done. Then in the 1980s came Margaret Thatcher and the dogma of neoliberalism, and the network of independent research stations was systematically trashed—privatized or closed down. The stream of insights has stopped. Now it is hard to find agricultural research of any kind, or research into food and nutrition, that is not paid for by some corporate. The most conspicuous innovation of the past 15 years has been the growth of GM crops—entirely speculative, but seen to be potentially lucrative. A succession of chief government scientists, none of them with any knowledge of agriculture, have queued up to tell us that we will all starve without them. The government itself is unbelievably ignorant, and none of its scientific advisers—or at least, the ones it takes notice of—seem to have any direct knowledge of farming, except of the highly industrialized kind that is conceived as a branch of big business. Well under 10 per cent of the research into GM crops, tens of millions of dollars' worth of it can be called independent.

Overall, the destruction of Britain's independent agricultural research can be seen as the most shocking act of state-sponsored vandalism since the dissolution of the monasteries in the 1540s, under Henry VIII. The independent research stations served Britain and the world very well indeed. So too did the old monasteries. They weren't just centres of prayer and contemplation, cut off from the world. For many of the people at large they were also the principal schools and hospitals, and were foci of serious farming. When they disappeared, the people suffered. But, as in modern times, their dissolution was cocooned in propaganda. The people were told that the monasteries were failing in their duty, that they had become corrupt, and so on. Almost all of this was lies, as Henry's own emissaries reported back to him. But so what? Nowadays, in similar vein, we are given to understand that Britain's old network of AFRC research stations and EHFs was 'inefficient' or some such, and that the government has done us all a favour by closing them down and handing over our food supply to Monsanto and Syngenta. Again, this is a straightforward lie—except that the politicians are so unaware of anything to do with food and farming that some of them apparently believe the propaganda is true.

Again, though, we find small organizations and individuals the world over continuing research of all kinds. As suggested earlier, we need not suppose that the farmers of the future have to conform to all the regulations that now allow farmers to be 'certified organic'. Nevertheless, organic farming in the future should be regarded as the default position—what should be done unless there is very good reason to do otherwise. We have stressed the need above all to farm according to the principles of sound biology—and indeed that we must embark upon 'The Age of Biology'. In practice, organic husbandry in its various forms takes us closest to that. Even in the days of the old AFRC, the powers-that-be neglected organic husbandry. We should be grateful therefore that over the past few decades various organizations worldwide have stayed on the case. In Britain these include the Soil Association and the Organic Research Centre (previously known as the Henry Doubleday Research Centre). There are comparable organizations oversees, not least in the United States and Germany.

Others are looking expressly at animal welfare. Near to where I live in Oxford is the Food Animal Initiative, FAI. It has a hybrid status both as a commercial farm and as a centre for research, mostly in conjunction with Oxford University (which owns the farm). Among other things it has pioneered methods of raising pigs (Gloucester Old Spots) not simply in family groups, but with several families together. 'Conventional' pig farmers might feel this is impossible— there would be all kinds of behavioural problems, from tail-biting to mass destruction of offspring. But with the right animals—a lot depends on simple selection—and husbandry it works beautifully. The contrast between the holiday-camp atmosphere of FAI's pigs and the concentration camp desperation of modern industrial pigs is absolute—and the idea that the latter is justified and indeed necessary because it is 'efficient' is yet another gross misunderstanding, not to say a lie. FAI is also pioneering agroforestry with chickens under young trees (chickens are basically woodland animals, who don't like to be in great open spaces) and producing breeds (by conventional breeding techniques) that can grow quickly without out-growing their strength and becoming crippled, as today's breeds commonly do.

In Suffolk Professor Martin Wolfe has his own farm at Wakelyns, where he has developed what promises to be a model of agroforestry which, with suitable local adaptation, could in principle serve the whole world. He grows trees in rows—willow and hazel for short-term use (for fuel and light fencing, and for browse and nuts); with serious hardwoods for wildlife, aesthetics, and long-term investment (oaks, hornbeam, and so on); or fruit trees—many different kinds in large numbers throughout the farm, but not close-packed as in an orchard, which helps to reduce disease. Between the rows the land can be cultivated any way the farmer wants—arable, horticulture, livestock of all kinds. Contrary to generally received opinion, all the crops benefit from the presence of the trees—and the livestock certainly do. All farm animals like shade and browse.

In the West Country (Devon) Martin Crawford has taken what he calls 'forest gardening' to a very high level. This is a form of agro-forestry producing food from the trees themselves—fruits and nuts—and from understories of shrubs and a ground cover of woodland horticultural crops such as strawberries. The result is brilliant.

In Britain, too, a group of farmers have formed the British Grass-fed Livestock Group, to explore the possibilities of raising cattle (in particular) on natural pastures—of vital concern to the future though much neglected at government level. Much of the necessary background thinking has been done not by 'official' research scientists but by an agricultural journalist, Graham Harvey, summarized in *The Carbon Fields* (Grassroots, Devon, 2008). In Oxfordshire, spreading into Wales and elsewhere, freelance archaeo-botanist John Letts is developing land races of ancient varieties of wheat and other cereals, some grown originally for thatching, but which also have some special nutritional qualities; showing (with help from other bakers) how they can produce excellent bread; and also showing how cereals can reasonably be grown on the small scale—even as a horticultural crop.

There are plenty of initiatives in the world at large, too. One I have spent time at is on the Atlantic coast of Brazil, where Robin and Binka Le Breton have established a 600-acre mixed farm where they hope not only to produce good food and employ local people but also to help restore some of the original Atlantic rainforest, now shamefully reduced.

These are just a few initiatives that come to mind. Worldwide there are hundreds. Governments may have abdicated from true governance, and the corporates that modern governments favour may continue to focus on their own advancement, but people world-wide are still on the case despite all the difficulties.

On the broad front
—the vital concept of 'Critical Mass'

Finally, there are many thousands of movements worldwide rooted in politics or economics, some of which are directly concerned with farmers and agriculture and some of which are broader in scope but obviously relevant. Obvious examples from Britain (just to give a flavour) are Friends of the Earth and Greenpeace; the Scottish Crofters Federation; Farm –an association for small farmers; and the New Economics Foundation, which at least has the wherewithal to devise a convincing economic base for Enlightened Agriculture, though it has not yet properly addressed the issue. Worldwide I am particularly interested in Via Campesina, a worldwide movement that operates on behalf of peasants—the vast group on which the whole world has depended this past 10,000 years, and always has been horribly underprivileged.

You will doubtless observe, however, that my list of good people doing good and pertinent things is perfunctory. Indeed, it is top-of-the-head. It mostly includes people and groups that I know person-ally, and in a few cases belong to in one capacity or another. Yet the list is enough to illustrate the three essential points.

First, the range of relevant initiatives is huge. Farming affects eve-rything else that happens in the world, and is affected by everything else, so how could it be otherwise? The freedom fighters and priests of South America who strive to ensure justice in countries ruled by 'colonels' and corporates with serious and typically mischievous in-puts from the rest of the world are very important. So too is the pri-mary school teacher in some genteel suburb who introduces his or her pupils to the joys of growing broad beans in yoghurt pots—it's the kind of activity that can trigger a career; that could indeed help to create the next, vital generation of farmers.

Secondly, concern with food and farming cuts across all other kinds of interest and predilection. Thus, organic farming may bring images to your mind of gentle figures with beards and sandals who you might reasonably suppose are 'left wing'. Indeed, organic farming and socialism do seem to slot together very neatly in various ways. Mahatma Gandhi comes to mind. Yet as Philip Conford relates in *The Origins of Organic Farming* (Floris Books, 2001), the pioneers of organic farming in Britain included some extreme and in some cases notorious right-wingers. It's amazing how quite different philosophies and worldviews can find themselves with common cause (although I do like to think as argued elsewhere that some worldviews are more conducive to useful action than others).

Thirdly, which I hope the above list at least hints at, the sheer *number* of people who are striving to do things differently, worldwide, is huge. Indeed the radical writer Paul Hawken decided at one point to make a list of all the world's NGOs (non-government organizations) who are trying to initiate new ways of doing things, not just in farming but across the board. He guessed, before he started, that there were probably a few thousand. He soon realised that there must be at least 10,000. Finally he concluded that there are probably at least 100,000 NGOs worldwide—organized groups who are actively trying to make a difference. One study in the US concluded that at least 40 per cent of people worldwide would like the world to be run along seriously different and more benign lines, and would throw their lot in with any convincing movement that could bring about the necessary changes.

I once had a conversation in Latvia with a young woman who was heavily involved with the Lutheran church. The Russians, she said, suppressed organized religion. But after they left (or at least, relinquished their political hold) people returned to Christianity in droves. All the churches of all denominations (mostly Lutheran but others too) were packed to the gunwales. Now (a few years later) the number attending church regularly had settled down to about 20 per cent. A pity, I said. Not at all, she said. Twenty per cent is enough—enough to make a huge difference to the society as a whole.

This is the point. What matters in creating long-term change, political and practical and social, is not majority, but critical mass. Twenty per cent of people roughly agreeing on a central idea and pulling with some coherence on the same rope can do all that is needed. Indeed there is formal evidence that as few as eight per cent of people properly motivated can change society profoundly.

In short, it's obvious that there are easily enough people out there who care about food and farming, and all the things that go with them—aesthetics, justice, way of life, wildlife—to form a critical mass that could change the whole world absolutely and forever. So why don't they?

Co-ordination is the point. No matter how many people are on side, they will not achieve anything, or very little, unless to some extent they work together. Co-ordination does *not* mean compliance. It simply means that people who may come from wildly different ways of life, and have (or appear to have) diametrically opposing views about, say, politics or religion, and almost anything else you might think of, find common cause. They can work together and change the world without swearing oaths of allegiance. The point is not to found a cult, but to create an alliance.

Co-ordination does not require a creed for all to subscribe to but it does need a rallying point, some easily identifiable philosophy that different people coming from different angles can feel comfortable with. Organic farming comes close to providing this, but it does not quite work. Too many people associate it with too much regulation. What can and does fit the bill, I suggest, is the broad notion of Enlightened Agriculture, aka Real Farming: loosely but well enough defined as 'agriculture that is intended expressly to feed people, well and forever, without wrecking the rest of the world'. There is a bit of a tautology in this of course, because agriculture that did wreck the rest of the world could not feed us forever—but I hope you can forgive this. It seems a good idea to spell out all the requirements.

For my own part I am, I regret, too old to start farming. I have in my time grown vegetables and fruit and kept chickens, but that was

30 years ago. I am older even than the average British farmer. What I have done, together with my wife, Ruth, helped by some kind volunteers and some professionals generously paid by a small charity, is establish The Campaign for Real Farming. The aim is to provide the rallying ground, the introductory service, and the debating chamber for all concerned people everywhere to share ideas and to form new alliances that really can push things forward.

The definition may be broad, but as discussed in the opening chapters of this book, the philosophy and the modus operandi that flow from it are clear. We have truly to care: we have to take it to be self-evident that it is *right* to want to feed everybody well, and to prevent mass extinction, and to do what is necessary to achieve this. In practice we need to farm according to the bedrock principles of sound biology. We need to define our economy according to the principles of common humanity and sound biology—and not allow the market to determine human values, or try to design farming and the fabric of the world according to corporate balance-sheets, or the ambitions of governments who feel it is their task in life to serve the corporates. We need science that is honest, and designed to serve humanity; in the context of agriculture, 'science assisted craft'. We need to base our agriculture on farms that are small to medium-sized, polycultural, minimum-input, and labour-intensive. We need a marketing network and food culture to match. All this follows from the central requirement, 'to feed all the world's people, well and forever, without wrecking the rest of the world'. But it can all be achieved in a near-infinity of different ways according to tradition and predilection and indeed whim.

The Campaign is built around a website: www.campaignforreal-farming.org. We also collaborated with Graham Harvey, and with Sam Henderson of Agrarian Renaissance to run the Oxford Real Farming Conference—a counter-voice to the established, annual, Oxford Farming Conference which, by and large, puts the establishment view. We held our first full meeting in Oxford in January 2010, with a follow up in London in May 2010; and the second ORFC in January 2011.

So where do we go from here? The website and its various spin-offs are growing apace. More and more good people are writing for us on issues across the board—the broadest issues of politics, economics, and science, to the minutiae of husbandry and cooking. We know already that the campaign has helped to form useful alliances between people (mainly farmers) who did not previously know each other. Growth could be exponential.

The dream, though, is for the website to metamorphose into the College for Enlightened Agriculture—although the title is not yet fixed and friends have urged us to call it 'The College for the New Agrarianism'. The aim is to pin down the myriad questions that need urgently to be addressed, and have been largely or completely neglected at government level for the past 40 years, or have simply been handed over to big business. These range from the science of GMOs to the feeding of cattle and pigs to the true impact of corporates in the world at large to the intricacies of land tenure and the practicalities of retail to the minutiae of baking bread. 'College' is defined in its traditional sense: not as a place where teachers dispense wisdom to pupils, but as a place where people identify the problems and freely share ideas. The website itself should become a virtual college. With time, with luck, the college could grow into a bricks-and-mortar establishment, with its own model farm (arranged along the lines of Wakelyns, though run by a co-operative of full-time and part-time farmers).

People are needed to make this work. The website as it stands could easily find work for half a dozen and a full-blown college would need far more. Volunteers are already proving invaluable but bona fide employees are needed. As in farming itself, a new generation is needed to pick up the baton and run with it. To move from where we are to a significantly higher plane the campaign needs money, and I don't have any, nor any expertise in raising it. But the seeds are there.

Please log on to www.campaignforrealfarming.org.

Pari Publishing is an independent publishing company, based in a medieval Italian village. Our books appeal to a broad readership and focus on innovative ideas and approaches from new and established authors who are experts in their fields. We publish books in the areas of science, society, psychology, and the arts.

Our books are available at all good bookstores or online at **www.paripublishing.com**

If you would like to add your name to our email list to receive information about our forthcoming titles and our online newsletter please contact us at **newsletter@paripublishing.com**

Visit us at **www.paripublishing.com**

Pari Publishing Sas
Via Tozzi, 7
58045 Pari (GR)
Italy

Email: info@paripublishing.com